The High Fibre, Low Calorie Diet and Recipe Book

P. RANI RAO
SANTOSH VAISH

Orient Longman

THE HIGH-FIBRE, LOW-CALORIE DIET AND RECIPE BOOK

ORIENT LONGMAN PRIVATE LIMITED

Registered Office
3-6-752 Himayatnagar, Hyderabad 500 029 (A.P.), INDIA
e-mail: cogeneral@orientlongman.com

Other Offices
Bangalore, Bhopal, Bhubaneshwar, Chennai, Ernakulam, Guwahati,
Hyderabad, Jaipur, Kolkata, Lucknow, Mumbai, New Delhi, Patna

© Orient Longman Private Limited, 2007

First Published 2007

ISBN 13: 978 81 250 3261 8
ISBN 10: 81 250 3261 4

Typeset by
Scribe Consultants
New Delhi

Printed in India at
Glorious Printers
Delhi

Published by
Orient Longman Private Limited
1/24 Asaf Ali Road
New Delhi 110 002
e-mail: delgeneral@orientlongman.com

Contents

Acknowledgements

First and the foremost I would like to thank Dr (Mrs) Salila Tiwari, Mr Saket and Mr Siddarth.

My thanks also go to Dr Rajesh, Dr Chandrasekhar, Dr (Mrs) Vijaya, Mr Sukh Deepak Malvai and to my aunt Mrs Lakshmi Roy for their support; and to my young friends Mrs Rajya Lakshmi, Mrs Preeti, Mrs Shanta, Mrs Lalitha, Ms Smitha, Mr Rain Kumar Kanduri and Mr Shailender.

I would like to make a special mention of my friend Mrs Kamala Bhaskar Rao who read the manuscript and tried out some of the recipes and my friend Kasturi Nori who encouraged me during its writing. It was she who introduced me to the Land Mark Education Forum which helped in my outlook towards the whole project of writing this book.

I sincerely appreciate and acknowledge the help and facilities given by my young friend Mrs Amita Roy. Her support and assistance and also the positive encouraging attitude of my friend Dr (Mrs) Shyamala Devi have gone a long way in my efforts to get the work published.

I thank my family members whole-heartedly especially my husband, daughter, son and son-in-law who have helped and stood by me in many ways throughout.

This book would not have been possible but for the valuable experience that I have been exposed to and learnt from my parents for the last fifty years. They too have been followers of the high-fibre, low-calorie diet for more than half a century and developed their own recipes towards this end which have found a place in this book. I owe my grateful thanks to them and humbly dedicate this book to them.

Dr (Mrs) P. Rani Rao

Acknowlededements

First of all I am very grateful to Almighty God and my Guruji Sh. Surinder Soni whose blessings took shape in the present form. I am very thankful to Dr. N.S. Adhikari, Hony. consultant Naturopathy for his guidance in Naturopathy, Yoga and diet. I am also thankful to my husband Dalip Vaish and my children Rahul and Nikita for their cooperation, moral support as they inspired me to complete the book. I am very grateful and thankful to Mr Saket and Mr Siddharth of Impress Offset, Noida, for their kind co-operation in getting this book in order.

Dr (Mrs) Santosh Vaish

Preface

"Let Food be thy medicine and let medicine be thy food"

Hippocrates

In this book, we have tried to abide by the above message by providing recipes that retain the medicinal and nutritive value of food while the same time ensuring that they are tasty.

When one goes to a doctor of any system of medicine, a question which is always posed by the patient is "What are we allowed to eat?" We have tried to answer this as well as the question of how to prepare the kind of food that facilitates faster recovery, and shortens the period of suffering.

This book is thus a modest attempt at presenting various ways of cooking that provide tasty, nutritious food to the healthy and also help in healing the sick. Persons desirous of losing weight will also benefit greatly from the cooking methods given in the book. As a result, these high-fibre, low-calorie recipes, if followed regularly, will provide good health and nutrition to everybody.

An effort has been made to demonstrate ways of cooking that require very little oil and spices as well as innovative uses (as dosas, curries, chutneys and snacks) of throwaway skins and seeds of vegetables using easily available Indian ingredients. A few novel ones are bajjis on the tawa, dosas made of the white portion of watermelon and stuffed vegetables with just one teaspoon of oil.

Furthermore, preparing these dishes with more oil and/or spices as is the normal practice will provide the taste of traditionally cooked dishes. Hence, this book can also be used as a regular book for every one. The inclusion of a detailed ten-language glossary of the different ingredients makes it easy to use.

Introduction

There are two main processes going on constantly in our body. These are ingestion and elimination (excretion). Ingestion means the intake of food for growth and maintenance of the body and the assimilation of the nutritive constituents from the food. Elimination is the removal of the waste products, dead cells and harmful (morbid) end-products of digestion from the body. There are four channels of elimination in our body, viz., the skin, the large intestine, the kidneys and the lungs, which eliminate all three states of morbid matter, gases, liquids and solids.

The proper intake of natural food and the proper excretion of morbid matter are necessary for a good and healthy body. These two processes are regulated by an adequate natural food intake, pure air, sunlight and yogasanas (or other exercises).

On the basis of their experiences and perceptions, our ancestors drew up several natural rules for a good and healthy life. Ancient Indian literature is thus a compendium of all the ingredients for leading a good, healthy life, including the correct natural foods, yogic exercises, etc.

In a meal, the health-promoting, nutritious component is supposedly provided by the raw foods. The remaining cooked portion should be either steamed, baked or boiled, and lightly seasoned. Though the cooked portion of a meal forms a minor, less importat part from the nutritional point of view, it is nonetheless, equally important from the psychological, aesthetic and social point of view. It is this part of the meal that gives us pleasure and satisfaction, which is essential for the mental health and sustenance of an individual. Cooking does make food soft, palatable and flavourful. It also makes some kinds of food more easily digestible. Starches and proteins, for example, are easier to digest on cooking.

Therefore, it is necessary to make the cooked food part of the menu, varied in taste and flavour as well as pleasing to the eye and palate. These factors greatly aid in the secretion of digestive enzymes; food thus properly digested and assimilated provides energy for our body.

Preparing and serving cooked food that is nutritious and pleasing to the eye and palate is an art. This can be done by using healthy ingredients and garnishing. This aspect though very significant, seems to be neglected by many dieticians. Very little information (and fewer recipes) is available on this, whereas there is plenty of literature on raw foods as well as on the tempting, delicious and appetizing, but less nutritious, junk foods. Various combinations of fats, starches, proteins, sugars, essences, preservatives, refined flour etc., which are less nutritious and a burden on our system, are used to prepare such food. Books also abound in low-fat (or low-calorie) cooking, but without the high- fibre component incorporated into it. It is this very aspect that our book deals with — how to cook tasty and healthy low-calorie, high-fibre food to sustain us, during health and sickness, for a lifetime.

While most fruits/vegetables are cooked without their skins, we can get the nutritive as well as the fibre value of the skins by cooking them separately. This way the recipes using peels add an extra dish to your menu! Vegetable peels can be made into a dry curry (as that of ridge gourd), chutney or dosa. They can be cooked and mashed into a pulp which can be used for thickening gravy or soup. Soups can be prepared separately with the uncooked skins using them as one of the ingredients. Skins of fruits can be eaten separately or pulped with any other fruit juice; skins of apples, guavas, etc., for instance, can be added to grapes while extracting grape juice. They can also be added to vegetable chutneys while grinding.

It is possible, though difficult, to live on a boiled or steam-cooked menu without fats for the duration of the treatment of a disease. The same is true of a slimming, health-promoting or cure programme. Perhaps one could manage for a few days or months, and on rare occasions, an year or two. Even during this period one would like a little variation in taste and flavour within one's dietary limits. But to live on such a bland and insipid diet, day in and day out for years together is just not possible for an ordinary person. It requires a yogi to do it. But not all of us are yogis. Quite a few of us, however, would like to lead a reasonably healthy, dsease-free life. We hope that the recipes in this book will go a long way in helping our readers achieve this aim.

1

A Balanced Diet

A balanced diet is the key to health and fitness. It balances the acid and alkaline elements of the blood, and thus contributes to good health. Intestinal flora should be 80 per cent alkaline and levels below this (i.e., higher acid levels) lead to ill health and disease which are often the result of an imbalanced diet. To maintain a healthy, alkaline composition of the blood, diet should be high fibre and low fat. Fruit and vegetables add to the alkalinity of the blood because they contain minerals in the form of organic salts. Though citrus fruit is acidic, these acids are converted into alkaline products (carbonates) in the body. Starches and proteins add to the acidity of the blood because of their acidic by-products. Carbohydrates give energy to the body, and break down into carbon dioxide and water. Carbon dioxide is acidic and must be neutralised by sodium for its successful elimination. Fruit and vegetables help to oxidise the waste products in body tissue, and feed and purify body tissue with organic salts like potassium. They also provide a good amount of anti-oxidants like lutrin and zeaxanthin, which neutralise free radicals before they can do any harm. Osteoporosis (brittleness of bones) is also kept at bay.

That is why both a high-fibre, low-fat diet and exercise are essential for health and for the treatment of many diseases and ailments, whether major or minor, acute or chronic, serious or casual (normal). This diet is advocated by the conventional medical and non-medical schools of thought for a variety of ailments like cancer, as well as for slimming and keeping fit and healthy. Various mass media advocate a 'high-fibre, low-fat diet' – in fact, not only low fat but low calorie also. While research into diet continues, it is now more or less widely accepted that diet *does* play a vital and pivotal role in the occurrence or non-occurrence, prevention or cure of an ailment or disease.

What then, is a high-fibre, low-fat diet? It is a diet that consists predominatly of fruit and vegetables, with their edible skin and seeds either cooked or uncooked, as well as whole nuts, cereals, and pulses in moderate amounts and a minimal intake of fat and oil.

It is said that an average individual needs just one tablespoon of fat per day, an amount available in natural form in the variety of food eaten every day. However, living on this fat source only is impossible from the social and psychological point of view. Therefore external fat has to be used within reasonable limits, to satisfy these requirements and the palate too.

A balanced diet should consist of about 40 per cent fruits, 30 per cent vegetables, 20 per cent cereals and pulses, 5 per cent carbohydrates and 5 per cent fats. It is advisable to have one meal consisting only of fruit everyday and one course of uncooked food as part of every meal. No food is exclusively protein, fat or carbohydrate; it is a combination of all these, plus fibre and other known and unknown substances.

2

Types of Food

HEALTH-BUILDING AND MUSCLE (BODY)-BUILDING FOOD

The food we eat can be classified into various categories, depending upon its characteristics. These are proteins, carbohydrates, fats, vitamins, minerals, fibre and water. One such classification divides food into health-building and muscle/body-building food.

Health-building Food

This consists of fruit, cooked or uncooked and green, leafy and other vegetables (excluding the starchy ones) such as cabbage, carrot, beans, pumpkin (red and ash), snake gourd, ridge gourd, lady's fingers, and varieties of cucumber. Foods belonging to this category fulfil the conditions listed earlier. Such foods are non-concentrated, have a high water content, are rich in vitamins and minerals, contain trace elements (which cannot be manufactured by the body and must therefore be regularly supplied from outside sources) as well as a lot of cellulose (roughage) which initiates peristaltic movement and therefore aids in digestion. Their high water content makes them lighter and easier to digest. The vitamins, organic minerals and salts they contain are alkaline and hence help to maintain the correct balance in body chemistry, besides ensuring the elimination of wastes from the body. Healthy blood is slightly alkaline (pH 7.4); as the percentage of alkalinity declines, the chances of ill health climb.

To get the full benefit from such food, it should, as far as possible be eaten fresh, whole (with skin) and uncooked. However, if eating fruit and vegetables uncooked and in bulk is not possible, they should be cooked conservatively. Garnishing and additives can be used if needed to enhance taste, nutritive value and flavour.

Muscle/Body-Building Food

This includes cereals like rice and wheat (the staple food of most), millets (cereal plants bearing small nutritious seeds like bajra, jowar etc.), pulses (all types), milk and milk products.

This category comes next in importance to health-building food. This food is useful when consumed in limited quantities but can be harmful to health when consumed in large quantities. This is because it is concentrated food with little water content and not as bulky as health-building food and requires more energy to digest. Hence it is more difficult to digest than health-building food. Cereals etc. should be eaten whole with skin intact because the skin has soluble fibre that helps reduce the level of cholesterol in the blood.

FIBRE

Fibre is the structural part of plants, the framework that supports and holds it together. It is also known as 'roughage' or 'bulk'. It includes non-digestible carbohydrates such as hemicellulose, lignin, pectin, gum and mucilage. Fibre is a macronutrient, but it is neither absorbed nor digested by the human stomach because it is resistant to digestive enzymes. It is just broken down by bacterial action, and the finely divided matter is then pushed out by the excretory system, acting as a natural laxative.

Fibre is found only in plant foods such as fruit and vegetables, especially in their indigestible stalks and peel, and in differing amounts in the husks of whole pulses (gram) and cereals.

There are many kinds of fibre and it can be broadly divided into water-soluble and water-insoluble fibre. Water-soluble fibre is found more in fruit and whole pulses, while water-insoluble fibre occurs more in vegetables and in most cereals. The 'inferior cereals' (like jowar, bajra and ragi) are in fact superior to the so-called 'higher' cereals like wheat and rice, because they are richer in the total amount of fibre they contain. The bran and germ of cereals contain a higher proportion of the minerals iron and phosphorous, as well as vitamin B complex (especially thiamine).

Fibre has many functions the most important of which are aiding in eliminating waste and curing constipation. Fibre helps in binding together the morbid (toxic) products of digestion inside the intestines and eliminating them, thus preventing their stagnation and putrefaction within the system. In this way it acts as a 'natural broom' removing harmful wastes from the body before they can cause any disease. It is believed by experts that cancer–causing agents are swept away quickly into the stool with fibre. A high fibre intake is associated with a significantly low incidence of colonic cancer. Water-soluble fibre is said to lower cholesterol by helping to reduce its production by the liver. Dietary fibre also washes away cholesterol before it can be assimilated. Fibre helps in retaining water inside the body because of its water-retention properties. It thus adds bulk to faecal matter as it passes through the intestinal tract. This keeps the faeces wet and soft, thus eliminating one important cause of constipation.

Fibre also stimulates muscles by helping in peristaltic movements, moving the waste products along quickly and regularly for elimination, thus preventing acid reflux, constipation and the necessity to strain while evacuating. Water-insoluble fibre is more useful in this respect than the water-soluble one, since the latter gets broken down into finer matter than the former and hence looses some of its binding and other mechanical properties.

By mopping up the cholesterol produced by the liver, fibre, especially the water-soluble variety, may prevent it getting absorbed into the blood and deposited in the arteries. This prevents diseases like arteriosclerosis, cardiovascular diseases, cancer of the colon and diabetes mellitus (by regulating the glucose metabolism). Certain fibre-rich vegetables contain chemicals called indoles which, according to laboratory tests, block the development of several types of cancer. These indoles are especially found in vegetables of the *cruciferous* family – broccoli, brussel sprouts, cabbage, cauliflower etc. It is also believed that a high-fibre diet helps to nullify the carcinogenic effects of fat. Hence, fruit (with water-soluble fibre) and vegetables (with water-insoluble fibre) in large proportion and whole cereals (wheat and rice—both with germ and bran), bran obtained of flour (water-insoluble fibre) and whole pulses like green gram, Bengal gram, and matki (water-soluble fibre) in moderate proportion should be eaten to get the advantage of both types of fibres.

Fibre is very good for those on a diet regime. It requires chewing, and tends to satisfy hunger without adding calories by swelling up in the body and creating a feeling of fullness and satisfaction.

Fibre should form just one important part of a balanced diet, chosen from wholesome food containing both types of fibre. Fibre should be eaten in the form of raw or lightly cooked vegetables, and where possible, unpeeled fruit as snacks or in meals and in salad every day. For even more fibre, look for wholegrain bread, cereals and use wholegrain flour and bran. Care must be taken while cooking, because overcooking destroys quite a lot of fibre.

However, too much fibre in the diet can do more harm than good, especially to people with digestive diseases. Symptoms ranging from painful gas (colic), nausea and vomiting, and diarrhoea to an inability to absorb essential vitamins and minerals may arise because of an excess of fibre in the system. Fibre may decrease the absorption of protein, fat, vitamins A and B^{12}, riboflavin, calcium, zinc, copper, magnesium and iron, as well as drugs of all types, lessening their pharmaceutical effectiveness. Beware of artificial fibre products. Eat natural food fibre that not only contains fibre compatible with the human system but also contains other vital nutrients, known as well as yet unknown.

FATS AND OILS

Fats and oils are technically called *lipids*, which are composed of three long fatty-acid chains attached to one glycerol molecule. These fatty acids vary in length and in degree of saturation. According to the degree of saturation, oils and fats are referred to as mono-unsaturated, polyunsaturated and saturated. Oils are liquids and fats are solids at room temperature.

Apart from supplying energy, fats help in forming the structural material of cells and tissues such as cell membranes and other organic components. They supply fat-soluble vitamins (vitamins A and E) and help in carrying these vitamins, as well as vitamins D and K. They also help in lubricating various types of processes within the body. They insulate the body against heat loss (by forming a thermal blanket) and also act as a reserve fuel to be used when needed.

Fats are supplied to the body by many items of food like butter, ghee (both contain vitamins A and D), cheese, milk, egg yolks, meat, oilseeds, nuts and soyabeans. The fats eaten in food or diet are called dietary fats. They occur naturally in nuts like groundnuts (peanuts), cashewnuts, almonds, and oilseeds like sesame and mustard. In fact, many cereals, pulses and vegetables contain some amount of fat, which is supposedly enough for the body, but the use of additional oil and fat is necessary for various reasons. Hence the aim should be to use not only a minimum of fat and oil, but also the least harmful of these, as excessive consumption leads to deleterious effects like obesity, hyperlipidemia, hypertension and cardiac problems.

Saturated fats are known to raise the cholesterol level in the blood. However, recent theories suggest that saturated fatty acids are good for growth and immunity and delay ageing as they contain free radical scavengers. Free radicals are formed inside the body during the various normal metabolic processes and are toxic by-products, and could be responsible for improper growth in children and low immunity and premature ageing in adults.

Polyunsaturated oils are believed to decompose easily when cooked as well as when stored (leading to peroxidation). They then form mutagenic and carcinogenic substances.

Routine cooking with oils hardly produces any harmful effects. Prolonged heating, re-using or overheating of oils, however, leads to charring, the production of harmful, oxidised products including ketones and peroxides and decomposition into unidentified polymerised products that are indigestible as well as toxic and carcinogenic. When oil becomes thick and rancid, the fat-soluble vitamins A and E are destroyed. Oils kept for a long time also become rancid and should not be used.

It is best to use oil or fat that is unrefined and locally available. Refined oils are 'dead oils', devoid of vitamins and minerals. The valuable vitamins and minerals of the source of the oil (seeds and nuts) are removed during the process of refining, not only by filtration and solvent extraction but also chemically. These chemicals are also harmful to health. Digestion of refined oils takes longer because their natural vitamins and minerals have been removed during the process of refining.

Comparison of the Properties of Oils (one tablespoon):

Type of oil	Unsaturated fatty acids		Saturated fatty acids (g)
	Monounsaturated (g)	Polyunsaturated (g)	
Best Oils			
Almond	10	2	1
Olive	10	1	2
Peanut	6	5	2
Good Oils			
Corn	3	8	2
Cottonseed	2	7	4
Safflower (kardai)	2	10	1
Sesame	5	6	2
Soyabean	3	8	2
Sunflower	3	9	1
Walnut	3	9	1
Worst Oils			
Coconut	1	—	12
Palm	3	1	7
Butter	3	1	7

The addition of synthetic vitamins to re-enrich the oil once again burdens the digestive system. Look for oils that are lower in saturated fatty acids and higher in unsaturated fatty acids, especially monounsaturated fatty acids.

PROTEINS, CARBOHYDRATES, VITAMINS AND MINERALS

Proteins

Proteins are the most important part of the dietary system and are essential for the growth, development, repair and maintenance of the body. Protein is a component of enzymes, haemoglobin (blood), hormones, muscles and hair.

The daily requirement of protein depends upon body weight.

Every kilogram of body weight ordinarily requires one gram of protein daily; pregnant women and growing children need more. Proteins are assimilated (absorbed into the blood) in the form of amino acids. On the basis of these essential amino acids, proteins are known as high-quality or low-quality proteins. Milk, almonds, soya beans and coconut are considered good sources of high-quality proteins whereas pulses, cereals and peas are low-quality proteins.

Protein deficiency causes weakness and tiredness. The toxic by-products of protein metabolism enter the blood-stream in the form of uric acid, urea and ammonia-like compounds. These toxins are responsible for gout, kidney damage, acidosis, arthritis, constipation, heart disease as well as other diseases.

Carbohydrates

Carbohydrates provide the body with both heat and energy. Sugars and starches are the commonest forms of carbohydrates in food.

A normal person requires 160–240 grams of carbohydrates daily.

Vitamins

Vitamins help the body process fats, carbohydrates and proteins. They protect the body against infections and promote good health.

Vitamin A

This vitamin builds resistance against infection and is essential for good eyesight, strong bones and general growth.

Its sources are almost all yellow-coloured fruit, green vegetables and milk.

Vitamin B-complex

This vitamin promotes general growth and health. It is essential for the normal functioning of the nervous and muscular systems. It is especially required for healthy skin, hair, teeth and mucous membranes as well as for blood formation.

Its sources are germs of cereals and sprouted cereal.

Vitamin C

This is important for healing, resistance to infection and general health.

The sources are Indian gooseberry (richest source), guava, sprouted pulses especially matki and green gram, lime, oranges and grapes.

Vitamin D

This assists in the absorption of phosphorus and calcium needed for the growth and development of bones and teeth.

Its sources are milk and milk products. The rays of the sun (ultraviolet rays) convert the cholesterol that is present in skin into vitamin D.

Vitamin E

This is essential for the proper functioning of blood, skin and the reproductive system.

Its sources are green leafy vegetables, whole grains, wheatgerm, vegetable oil and ghee.

Vitamin K

This is essential for clotting of blood and the proper functioning of the liver.

The sources are cabbage, tomato, spinach, potato, wholegrains, wheatgerm and wheat bran. It is also produced in the intestines.

Minerals

Although important, lower quantities of minerals are required for the growth, development and maintenance of the body. Calcium, potassium, sodium, magnesium and phosphorus are the important basic requirements of the body. Other essential minerals are, iodine, copper, iron, manganese, zinc, chromium and selenium. Calcium and phosphorus are needed for the proper growth and development of bones. Calcium is also very good for vitality, enzyme activity and blood ailments. Iodine is essential for the functioning of the thyroid gland. Copper helps in the absorption of iron. Chromium helps curb high blood pressure. Manganese helps in the action of enzymes and the clotting of blood.

Magnesium aids the functioning of muscles and nerves. Iron is required for the formation of haemoglobin in the blood; its deficiency causes anaemia.

Potassium is a very important mineral for the normal functioning of the nerves, enzymes and muscles including heart muscles. Potassium prevents sodium from raising blood pressure. Sodium is essential for maintaining the water balance in the body.

Minerals are sourced from green, leafy vegetables, wholegrains, milk, bran and mushrooms.

CHOLESTEROL

Cholesterol is a stable yellowish-white waxy or fatty substance insoluble in water but soluble in fats. Cholesterol is not present in plants or plant products. Thus all oils including almond, peanut and seed-butter (e.g. peanut butter, soya butter, hazelnut butter, sesame butter), do not contain cholesterol. It is important to note that although some vegetable oils like coconut oil and palm oil do not contain cholesterol, they nevertheless clog the arteries since they contain a predominant amount of saturated fatty acids (see table on p. 8). They are difficult to digest and get deposited in the walls of the arteries.

Cholesterol is found only in animals and animal products like meat, eggs, seafood and dairy products. It is present in the body in all the cells and body fluids (except in the cerebrospinal fluid). The human body produces most of its own cholesterol requirements, in the liver. Some cholesterol also enters the body through food like butter, cheese, eggs and fatty meals (especially those that contain saturated fats). The liver processes the extra cholesterol (contained in food) and destroys it. Thus cholesterol enters the body chiefly through animal products.

Fats, oils, cholesterol, waxes or the decomposed products of fats/oils (that is, fatty acids and esters of fatty acids) are all termed lipids. They are insoluble in water and therefore not easy to digest, since digestive juices are aqueous and the process of digestion takes place in an aqueous medium. Lipids therefore need special mechanisms to make them digestable. Some are emulsified into diglycerides, monoglycerides, fatty acids and glycerol. During the course of metabolism (in simpler terms, digestion) these unmetabolised/undigested fats/oils/cholesterol in association with the proteins of the body form three kinds of lipoproteins. These are High Density Lipoproteins (HDL), Low Density Lipoproteins (LDL) and Very Low Density Lipoproteins (VLDL), formed through the action of various enzymes in the liver. These three different classes of lipoproteins are based on differing ratios of lipids and proteins resulting in varying molecular weights.

Among them HDL is the most beneficial because it acts as a scavenger, while VLDL is the most dangerous. Lipids, both fats or oils as well as cholesterol, get carried into the blood in the form of HDL, LDL or VLDL.

Only a small portion of the lipoproteins is required by the body. The excess, as well as the fatty acids, get stored in the body, leading to the narrowing and hardening of the walls of the arteries and the heart. This results in high blood pressure and cardiac problems. Some lipoproteins, which are undigested and unabsorbed, are removed by faecal excretion. Normal blood cholesterol level varies between 150–200 mg per 100 ml of blood.

It is now believed that a high-fibre diet envelops the cholesterol molecules, helping to excrete them along with the fibre. Such a diet also inhibits the production of cholesterol by the body. Good or bad cholesterol, is not consumed simply because HDLs and LDLs are not found in food. However, HDL levels can be raised through meditation, exercise, losing weight, abstaining from smoking and alcohol and eating plenty of fruit and vegetables. Spinach, apples, raw onions (whole or juiced) and raw garlic (whole, juiced or crushed) reduce cholesterol levels. Thus a high-fibre diet partly nullifies the intake of moderate amounts of cholesterol.

SPROUTS

Pulses are concentrated food and rather difficult to digest due to their high protein content, but when eaten whole, with their skins intact, they are easier to digest and are more nutritious. The skins provide soluble roughage, vitamins and minerals.

When pulses are sprouted, their vitamin and mineral content and a high quantity of enzymes, which are necessary for good digestion, are produced inside the germinating grain to provide for the growing embryo. In fact, their vitamin content especially of vitamins A, B and C is as high as in fruit. They also contain calcium, magnesium, phosphorus, chlorine, potassium, sodium, silicon and some mineral compounds. Therefore, sprouted pulses are easier to digest than unsprouted pulses. They are tiny, live vitamin factories, far superior to the synthetic vitamin tablets sold by chemists.

Sprouted pulses must be eaten when the sprouts are small (2–3 mm in length). At that point in time, their vitamin C content is at its maximum. As the length of the sprouts increases, the vitamin C content decreases, with a corresponding increase in the carbohydrate content. In fact, it is believed that the vitamin C content starts deteriorating after 48 hours. Besides vitamin C, other vitamins are also produced during germination. These are mostly present in the grain and not in the sprout. The size of the grain becomes smaller and smaller as the sprout grows and hence the amount of vitamins also decreases. So only fresh pulses and pulses with small-sprouts should be eaten.

Matki (moth) has the highest amount of vitamin C, followed by green gram, Bengal gram and green peas. Vitamin C is destroyed by cooking and enzymes are also sensitive to heat. Hence, sprouted pulses should be eaten raw or subjected to minimum cooking. If they have to be cooked, steaming is the best method of preserving vitamin C.

The daily requirement of vitamin C is 30–40 milligrams. This can be obtained from a quarter of a guava (20 grams), one eighth of an amla (7 grams), 5 bananas, 60 grams of papaya, 25 grams of coriander leaves, 30 grams of cabbage, 20 grams of knol-khol leaves, 35–45 grams of other leafy vegetables or 60 grams of sprouted green gram (moong) etc.

3

The Digestive Process

The human body is composed of many kinds of tissues. Whether awake or sleeping, some parts of the body are always working and continuously wearing out. Material is needed to repair this wear and tear. It is also needed for growth and, for supplying heat and energy to the body. This material is found and obtained from the food eaten.

Food by itself cannot be used by the body for a number of reasons. It must be broken down, that is, digested into a form which can be utilised by the body. Complex food is broken down by mechanical (chewing) and chemical reactions into simpler food material. Only these simple compounds are accepted by the blood stream for feeding the cells. Starches and sugars get converted into simple sugars like glucose and fructose, fats into fatty acids and glycerol and proteins into amino acids.

This process takes place in the digestive system, which consists of various organs that do this job. Some food gets digested only in a particular part of the digestive tract. Others get digested in more than one part of the digestive system; for example, starch digestion starts in the saliva of the mouth; whatever remains undigested, goes into the stomach and gets digested there. Further digestion takes place in the duodenum by the pancreatic juices. Carbohydrates (sugars, non-sugars and starch) are mainly digested in the mouth and duodenum, proteins in the stomach and fats in the duodenum.

The digestive system is also called the gastro-intestinal tract or alimentary canal. It consists of the mouth, esophagus, stomach, small and large intestines and several glands such as the salivary glands, liver and pancreas, which provide fluids (enzymatic juices) that help to break down food. The digestion of food takes place mainly in the mouth, the stomach and the small intestine. The absorption of digested, solid foods takes place mainly in the small intestine, and of digested liquid food in the large intestine. The whole alimentary canal is lined with mucous membrane which has an immense number of glands.

Food is first chewed or masticated in the mouth into finer particles, so that a larger surface area of the food is exposed to the action of the enzymes that are secreted by the salivary glands. The two enzymes, ptyalin and amylase, act upon starch and convert it into maltose, a complex sugar. The chewed food is then pushed via the esophagus into the stomach where it is churned. The innumerable glands in the stomach release the enzymatic juices that act upon the food chemically. Masticated food is mashed and mixed with these juices (especially the acidic gastric juice that contains pepsin and hydrochloric acid) into a finer state. Pepsin and hydrochloric acid mainly break up proteins into peptides and peptones, carbohydrates into simpler sugars and partially break down fats into fatty acids and glycerol.

When the stomach has done its work, the food passes in an almost liquified state into the duodenum or upper part of the small intestine. Digestive juices from the pancreas and bile from the liver pour into the small intestine through two small ducts. These alkaline juices further break down the food into a form that the cells can use. Pancreatic juice contains enzymes like trypsin and hormones like insulin which complete the digestion of proteins, fats and carbohydrates. Bile (stored in the gall bladder, situated below the liver) contains inorganic salts, bile pigments, bile salts (cholesterol, etc.) that help in digestion of fats. The fatty acids thus formed are dissolved in an almost detergent-like solution of bile salts, and get carried to various parts of the body. Bile also helps in the elimination of waste products from the blood. As the semi-liquid food passes through the small intestine, the useful solid particles are almost entirely absorbed by the small intestine, and, are then distributed throughout the body by the blood and the lymphatic fluid. The rest of the food continues through the small intestine and into the large intestine. The useful liquid portion, including water, is absorbed in the large intestine and passes from there into the cells of the body. The remaining solid matter, consisting of cellulose and dead bacteria, passes into the lower part of the large intestine (colon) and accumulates in the rectum, which is at the end of the colon. It is stored there till it is excreted as faeces. Faeces are brown due to the presence of bile pigments. Clay coloured or pale stools suggest a liver dysfunction or an obstruction to the flow of bile.

If the elimination of unused food is incomplete because of defective bowel movements and the malfunctioning of the eliminative organs, these waste products get stored within the body. Nature has a wonderful way of protecting the human body from damage and so it stores these waste products in unimportant and non-vital parts of the body. If there is an excessive build- up of these poisonous wastes then they attack vital organs like the heart and lungs.

It is very interesting to note that during digestion, complex foods (carbohydrates, proteins, fats, etc.) are broken down into simpler substances like simple sugars, amino acids, fatty acids and glycerol. Only the food in these forms is absorbed in the small and large intestines. Absorption is followed by assimilation. In this process the simple substances are reconverted to the starting and other materials needed by the body for proper functioning. For example, sugars (digested parts of polysaccharides) are reconverted into complex polysaccharides and glycogen in the liver, amino acids (digested products of proteins) into different proteins which are needed for building up body tissue and enzymes (which are proteinaceous) and fatty acids and glycerol into fats.

4

Tips for Improving Health

Any kind of food can, of course be chosen keeping in mind parameters like age, sex, climate, physical activity, health level desired and taste.

A few tips regarding the choice of food, the way it should be handled before, during and after cooking are given below:

Food should be eaten, as far as possible, in its most natural form, either raw or minimally cooked, and preferably with the skin on (whenever edible). This will contribute greatly towards good health.

Every food product should be taken whole, or in as complete a form as practical. Wholeness is wholesomeness. When wheat flour is deprived of its bran by sieving, when rice is milled and polished and deprived of its vitamin-and mineral-rich outer layer, when milk is boiled or pasteurised, when vegetables and fruit are peeled, they all lose their wholesomeness. It is well to remember that a significant portion of the nutrients lie on and under the skin. If vegetables have to be peeled and pulses and cereals deskinned, then the peel and skin should be used to make chutneys, dosas, and curries as given in various recipes in this book.

Always use fresh vegetables and fruit, whether raw or cooked. Because food is organic, the moment a fruit or vegetable is removed from the parent plant, the nutritive elements begin to decay. Over-ripe fruits should never be eaten.

Storing entails a loss in nutrients as well as bulk because of a decrease in the water content through evaporation or drying. Keep food for short periods in air tight/vacuum-sealed containers, or in a refrigerator.

Wash vegetables and fruit well. Fruit and vegetables are commonly sprayed with harmful insecticides that are deposited as a visible, and sometimes invisible, white powder. Simply immersing them in water and then draining the water cannot effectively remove the powder. Fruit and vegetables should therefore be thoroughly scrubbed before being used.

Wash vegetables and fruit before cutting. Once they are cut, some of their valuable vitamins and minerals start 'oozing out'. Since some of these are soluble in water, the nutrients are lost when the water is thrown away. Washing cut vegetables and fruit will result in the cut portion becoming contaminated by dirt and insecticides. It is therefore more hygienic to wash vegetables and fruit before cutting, rather than after.

Cut vegetables and fruit into large pieces. The bigger the piece of the vegetable or fruit, the better will be its retention of vitamins and minerals, as oxidation alters their properties and food value. In some cases, as for example, banana, apple and brinjal, the change is perceptible, but in others, the change is not so obvious. This is why almost all cut vegetables and fruit acquire a slight tinge when left cut.

Consume the vegetables or fruits immediately after cutting, as oxidation results in the loss of nutrients.

Do not discard the leaves of beetroot, carrot, radish, cauliflower and the outer green leaves of cabbage. They are a good source of many nutrients, like vitamins A and C. Use them raw or conservatively cooked, alone or in combination with other vegetables or pulses.

Eat vegetables raw whenever possible, to get maximum advantage of their nutritive elements. Radish, turnip, carrot, tomato, coriander leaves, cucumber, cabbage, onion and its shoots, etc. can be eaten raw in the form of salad.

Avoid vegetables and fruit that have an overgrown appearance. It is now well-known that food grown with the help of chemical fertilizers is not as good or nutritious as that grown with natural organic manure. One may even notice a deterioration in the taste of such products. A plausible explanation for this could be that a part of the chemical fertiliser gets absorbed into the vegetable, fruit or seed through the capillary action of the plant. To dilute the toxicity of the chemical in them, they just grow in size, without a corresponding increase in nutrients.

Buy only seasonal vegetables. Nature produces an abundance of certain vegetables and fruit in certain seasons, when the environmental conditions are optimal for their growth. Moreover, growing vegetables out-of-season requires the application of special methods of cultivation and care (like fertilisers, cold storage and the use of preservatives), which are not conducive to health.

Avoid excessive use of baking soda/powder. It destroys most of the vitamin B complex in food, besides destroying enzymes. By making the food porous, it also helps in greater absorption of oil or fat through the air holes. A few pulses like bean seed (rajma) and gram (kabuli chana) are normally cooked with soda to reduce their cooking time. Prior soaking in water till they soften and swell, as well as utilising the water in which they were soaked for cooking, can reduce the cooking time. It is better to just extend the cooking time rather then use baking soda/powder.

Avoid adding salt or masalas right at the beginning when cooking vegetables. The natural combination of nutrients is altered by cooking with salt, and the body absorbs nutrients best in their natural combinations. Cooking vegetables with salt is common practice, since it makes the vegetables much tastier. However, it is better to avoid doing this because this practice has some disadvantages:

(i) Salt is consumed in greater quantities if the vegetables are cooked with salt right from the beginning. This is because salt penetrates inside the pieces during cooking and gets absorbed. If, however, salt is added after the vegetable is cooked, less salt will be needed since most of the salt will remain only on the surface of the vegetable. This is evident from the taste also, when both methods are compared.

ii) Salt makes a vegetable tastier, thereby promoting one cause of overeating.

iii) The added sodium salt and the potassium, calcium and magnesium salts present in the vegetable will all undergo change. These salts will thus not be available in their natural states.

Boiling, baking, steaming and simmering are the conservative ways of cooking. It is advisable to start on high heat and then switch to low heat while cooking vegetables. This increases the chances of the nutrients staying within the vegetables when they are cooked, as the outer surface gets cooked first, retaining its nutrients inside. **Do not overcook vegetables.**

Avoid using heavy and pungent spices with a lot of oil or fat and garam masala. Such things may be used only occasionally. At such times, the ill effects of these should be compensated by eating salads or a very lightly seasoned dish that is cooked conservatively to retain its nutrients.

Excessive use of fat results in flatulence and other digestive disorders, obesity, diabetes and heart disease. The use of too many/much of spices and condiments destroys the natural flavour and taste of food. Spices and condiments also irritate the mucous membrane of the digestive tract and this affects the tone of the digestive system, causing irritable bowel syndrome, ulcers and a burning sensation in the rectum and anal regions.

Serve food warm and fresh, to avoid it becoming stale and unhygienic. Cooked food deteriorates at a faster pace than uncooked food. It is therefore best to eat freshly-cooked food, and that too, as soon as possible.

Avoid reheating food. Reheating results in a greater loss of nutrients, besides changing the original taste, colour and flavour of food. If food has been refrigerated, take it out of the refrigerator an hour or so before eating so that it comes to room temperature on its own.

Use sprouts of pulses and grams in cooking as they are a fairly rich source of proteins. Germinated grams and pulses have, besides other vitamins, quite a lot of vitamin C and enzymes. The quality of protein therein also improves, and its carbohydrate is more easily digestible.

The inorganic sodium salt, called common salt, that is added to food is not needed by the body. All the sodium salt needed is available in vegetables and fruit, and in other whole, natural foods like cereals and pulses. Salt, on the contrary, acts as a burden on the body by irritating the mucous membranes, hardening them in due course and thereby hampering their normal functions. Use as little common salt as possible. Excessive consumption is harmful; it leads to water retention in the body, swelling of the legs, high blood pressure and kidney disorders, among other things.

Use as far as possible, unrefined, whole food items in place of refined ones, which are heavy on digestion. Use wholewheat flour in place of refined flour and whole cereals and pulses rather than husked ones, as the bran and germ of cereals contain iron, phosphorus and vitamin B complex, and also add to dietary fibre. Use (1) jaggery (which contains some iron) in place of sugar; (2) unrefined oils, cream or butter instead of refined oils, ghee or hydrogenated oil; and (3) skimmed milk instead of whole milk.

Do not eat too often or too much. This results in the digestive system becoming overloaded and an extraordinary expenditure of the body's vital power. Excessive or wrong food is a tax on vitality. By eating the right type of food in its natural form this vital power, which would otherwise have been wasted, is conserved.

Do not eat when mentally upset or physically unwell. Avoid harsh words, negative thoughts, unpleasant conversation, bingeing after prolonged fasting and eating when depressed, as these upset the body's system. A pleasant atmosphere while eating is conducive to good digestion.

If one particular meal has been very heavy, skip the next meal or wait till the previous meal has been completely digested. Do not eat or drink anything except water. Give the stomach a complete rest for a few hours. The following meal should consist only of fresh fruit, fruit or vegetable juice and salads. These will supply the body with the nutrients and fibre that were lacking in the previous heavy meal. There should always be at least a five to eight hour gap between two heavy meals.

Seasoning should be done with minimum oil (½–1 tsp). Contrary to popular belief, onions do not need much oil for frying. To season with just ½–1 tsp oil, add onion bits, sprinkle a little water (if needed), cover with a lid on which water is poured and cook on a low fire.

Onions fried as described above can be substituted for coconut. The reasonably tender white portion (kernel) of tender coconuts can be ground and used. The fat content in this is much less than in the usual (mature) coconuts and is in a more easily digestible colloidal state.

5

Food Recommended for Various Diseases

It is advisable to follow a restricted diet during various ailments so that the duration of suffering, and the drug regimen, can be minimised. During an illness the body becomes weak, that is, low in vitality, and hence unable to digest routine food. At such a time, the food should be simple, easy to digest and in small portions. Fatty, fried and spicy food should be avoided. Preserved or refined food, junk food, pickles, artificial drinks, sweets and stimulants like coffee and tea, should be severely restricted.

Drinking, smoking and other narcotics (tobacco, pan masala etc.) should be strictly avoided as they aggravate suffering and neutralise the action of the medicine.

Most diseases are mainly due to a deficiency of organic minerals, vitamins, fibre and water that form the main constituents of fruit and vegetables. A plentiful supply of these helps in the proper functioning and repair of any part of the body. The system gets greater *prana sakti* (vital power) to deal with its physical and mental state, as well as external factors like bacteria and viruses, injuries, and unsuitable weather conditions, which are the pre-disposing causes of diseases. These factors will have a minimal effect if the body is well-nourished. An underlying state of malnutrition, wrong eating habits, an unhealthy life style and a defective diet must be avoided, as this makes the body an easy target for bacteria and viruses. Daily consumption of a variety of fruit and vegetables is recommended, to provide the body with its defence mechanisms. In addition, some specific food is recommended for particular ailments, to make up for specific deficiencies and neutralise some undesirable products of metabolism, such as, iron-rich foods like dates for anaemia, insulin-rich food like bitter gourd and sprouted grains for diabetes and uric acid-dissolving food like raw potato for arthritis, rheumatism and gout.

In general, vitamins A and C help in healing and fighting infection. Hence daily doses of these are recommended. Fruit and vegetables taken in their raw state as juice are ideal (when diluted and sipped slowly to secrete enough saliva). Raw juice provides a high content of assimilable nutrients that the body can immediately absorb, assimilate and use for its nourishment and repair. The body needs minimum energy to digest them; no digestive energy is expended in extracting the vital nutrients from the huge amounts of raw food that would otherwise have had to be consumed to get these extra large doses. The vital power within the body can thus be utilised for other functions or repairs. The next best way of obtaining large doses of nutrients is to eat vegetables as raw salads. Salads supply nutrients in their natural form, as well as bulk. They supply a lot of fibre, which is helpful in bowel movements and is a natural broom for body wastes in the intestines. To get a sufficient supply of nutrients a fairly good helping of salad needs to be eaten daily. This, however, is often difficult. A reasonable portion of salads with each meal, though, will provide a certain amount of nutrients and plenty of roughage. A third way of deriving the benefit of vegetables is to cook them conservatively, such that there is minimum loss of nutrients while at the same time retaining a variety in taste, flavour and attractiveness, which are all important for making food appealing.

ANAEMIA

Anaemia is a condition in which the haemoglobin content of blood falls below the normal range. The possible causes for this include a deficiency in the raw materials required for the production of blood in the bone marrow, an excessive loss of blood due to injury, excessive bleeding during menstruation and piles and the destruction of blood in the body itself due to cancer, malaria, and tuberculosis.

The main symptoms of anaemia are breathlessness, fatigue, weakness, pale skin and abnormal menstruation in women. Sometimes there is also pain in the bones or brittleness in nails.

Since anaemia is essentially due to a low iron content in the blood, organic iron and vitamin C help to treat and prevent it. Organic iron helps to stimulate the formation or production of red blood cells (haemoglobin) in the blood, reactivates them, supplies the necessary amount of oxygen to the body and thus helps in normal breathing. Vitamin C also induces the formation of new red blood cells, thus enriching the haemoglobin content of the blood. Green mango, Indian gooseberry and sprouts of germinated pulses are good sources of this vitamin.

Recommended Food

Fruit: Orange and papaya (1 glass of orange juice or a papaya boosts the absorption of vegetable iron by 200–500 per cent); tomato juice (is twice as rich in iron as milk, and five times richer than egg white); pomegranate and carrot juice; figs; grapes; ripe banana; dates; water melon; jambul fruit; pineapple; apple; apricot; almond; dried peaches and dried prunes.

Vegetables: Alfa-alfa; amaranth leaves; green coriander; Bengal gram leaves; beetroot, cabbage; fenugreek leaves; lettuce; mustard leaves; onion; spinach; raw banana; other green leafy vegetables (which are also rich in the minerals that reduce stomach acidity); carrot; spinach; radish; cucumber and ash gourd.

Other items: Black sesame seed (as good as an iron tonic); soyabeans; wholegrain cereals; jaggery-based sweets and wheatgrass juice.

ARTHRITIS

Arthritis is a disorder of the joints and their muscular surroundings. The causes of arthritis may be, among other things, rheumatic fever, uric acid deposits, osteoarthritis (degenerative joint disease, and brittleness of bones), injury, allergy or drug reaction, blood disorders and hormonal abnormalities. While it could be present in family history, physical or emotional shock and exposure to cold or wet conditions are also important factors in this regard. Common types of arthritis are gout, osteoarthritis, rheumatoid arthritis and rheumatic fever. Osteoarthritis is the commonest form and generally attacks people over forty years of age. In this disease, knees and weight-bearing joints are generally affected. Sometimes overgrown bones are also observed. Rheumatoid arthritis, in which the fingers are mainly affected and become disfigured, is less common. It can be cured and prevented by a strict diet regimen, exercise and natural therapies like water therapy.

Arthritis is basically due to an accumulation of uric acid and calcium in the joints and their muscular surroundings, which prevent their normal movement, leading to swelling and pain in these areas. To prevent and cure arthritis, food that dissolves accumulated uric acid must be consumed, and further accumulation of uric acid must be prevented. This is accomplished by eating food that is rich in alkaline mineral salts. These salts neutralise the acidic by-products of metabolism, including uric acid, thus relieving stiffness, swelling and pain in the joints. Vitamin C is chiefly responsible for preventing and curing inflammation of the joints.

Recommended Food

Fruit: Banana (contains a high-grade protein that includes three of the essential amino acids); grape; guava; raisins; strawberry; cherry (inhibits the deposition of uric acid); musk melon (keeps the excess calcium in suspension form, and is especially good for osteoarthritis); fig; black currant; apple (checks the formation of uric acid in the system); pomegranate and Indian gooseberry.

Vegetables: Cucumber; bitter gourd; beetroots; spinach (eliminates toxic uric acid from the system and helps to provide useful minerals); carrot; bottle gourd; amaranth; goosefoot white; fenugreek leaves; soya leaves; cabbage; coriander leaves; parsley; radish (especially its juice with cane sugar or jaggery); celery etc.

Other items: Garlic and its leaves (contain anti-inflammatory properties and help in curing swelling and pain); whole (unpeeled) raw potato juice (1 or 2 teaspoonfuls to be taken before meals, since it dissolves uric acid); celery (due to its high organic sodium content, which reduces calcium deposits in the joints); celery juice (can be combined with carrot juice); fenugreek seeds; saffron; honey (reduces uric acid); sprouted wheat and green gram (supply enzymes); lime (its high citric acid content prevents the deposition of uric acid); wheatgrass, walnut, tea of alfa-alfa, coconut water and lemon grass.

ASTHMA AND OTHER RESPIRATORY DISEASES

Respiratory diseases are increasingly common nowadays due to air-pollution, general illness, smoking, allergies, and bacterial and viral infections. These diseases include asthma, adenoids, sinusitis, bronchitis, pneumonia and tuberculosis. Respiratory diseases are essentially due to an accumulation of mucous in the respiratory tract.

In order to cure and prevent these diseases, the accumulated mucous in the respiratory tract must be dealt with, and further accumulation of mucous prevented. Food rich in vitamin C help toward this end. The intake of mucous-forming foods (like rice and grains) must be restricted.

Recommended Food

Fruit: Fig (eliminates or expels phlegm), Indian gooseberry (provides vitamin C), grape, orange juice (loosens mucous or phlegm and prevents secondary infections), pomegranate, dates and papaya.

Vegetables: Mint (liquifies sputum, gives strength to the lungs, and increases the body's resistance to infection), spinach (especially for bronchitis and tuberculosis; increases the body's resistance to infection), red cabbage, tomato, bitter gourd, carrot, radish, celery, coriander leaves and cucumber.

Other items: Garlic (taken with boiled milk at night), ginger (liquifies sputum, gives strength to the lungs, increases the body's resistance to infections), onion (especially in bronchitis), fenugreek seeds, asafoetida, saffron, aniseed (expels phlegm from the bronchial tubes due to its essential oil. This oil is lost if aniseed is boiled for too long), juice of unpeeled raw potato and apple, juice of carrot, beetroot, and cabbage and leafy vegetables, garlic juice, and juice of bitter gourd with honey.

Honey immediately reduces inflammation and coughing spasms. It has a fatal effect on germs as a result of its moisture-absorbing capacity. Soak a few slices of onion overnight in honey, then take a spoonful of the mixture twice a day.

COMMON COLD AND COUGH

The common cold is a viral infection of the upper respiratory tract. Sneezing, running nose, watering eyes, headache, body pain, throat pain and chills are the main symptoms. When accompanied by fever, the condition turns into influenza. The influenza virus is transmitted through the breath of infected persons. Exposure to cold or sudden changes of temperature and general weakness may prolong the suffering. Natural food therapy helps in a quick recovery, and also serves as a preventive measure.

The common cold is basically due to a sore and inflamed mucous membrane in the upper respiratory tract, especially the throat and nose. The soreness and inflammation is due to the acidic by-product of decomposing mucous, which provides a fertile medium for the common cold virus.

The common cold is best prevented by a daily, plentiful supply of of vitamins A and C. Once a cold has set in, however, the decomposition of mucous in the respiratory tract must be stopped and the accumulated mucous eliminated. The body must be helped to eliminate the accumulated mucous by thinning it, drying the mucous and then shrinking the mucous membrane (thus relieving swelling and inflammation). Both vitamins A and C increase the body's resistance to infection while it breaks up the mucous and eliminates toxins from the system.

Recommended Food

Fruit: Indian gooseberry, black currant, pineapple, raw papaya, lime juice with warm water, honey, mango (vitamin A), orange (vitamin C), apple (pectin), fig (relieves a fit of coughing) and pomegranate.

Vegetables: Carrot, beetroot, tomato, capsicum, onion, raw papaya, cabbage and radish; and soups made from these vegetables.

Other items: Garlic (dislodges phlegm, is antibacterial and fights against infection), fresh turmeric juice or the powder of dried turmeric mixed with warm milk (checks mucous coming out of nose, throat or wind pipe, shrinks mucous membrane, reduces phlegm); ginger juice (as in ginger tea, i.e., ginger boiled in water with an equal quantity of basil leaves); honey (soothes the sore and inflamed mucous membrane of the upper respiratory tract); warm water mixed with honey and lime juice in the morning; carrot juice with a tablespoon of garlic or onion juice, basil and achamana (small quantity of water sipped slowly several times during the day).

CONSTIPATION

Constipation is not actually a disease but a condition following the malfunctioning of the system. Constipation leads to many afflictions like rheumatism, piles, fissures, appendicitis and even cancer. Constipation may be functional, that is, rectal inactivity due to faulty habits or over-sedation; and intestinal inactivity due to an insufficient food intake, a sedentary lifestyle, insufficient cellulose fibre in food and the use of certain drugs like iron, opium and morphine. Constipation may also be due to endocrinal malfunction, hypothyroidism, diabetes mellitus or pressure on the rectum due to a prolapsed uterus or tumours. Generally, constipation occurs due to a lack of fibre and mineral water in the diet, insufficient physical exercise, inadequate sleep, mental tension and a low intake of water.

Those suffering from constipation pass hard, dry and insufficient stools, and suffer from headache, a feeling of heaviness, lethargy and loss of appetite. Retention of stools may lead to the poisoning of the whole system, resulting in a host of other problems.

Laxatives and purgatives are harmful to the system. No medicine can cure constipation without proper dietary intake. There should be a balance between physical activity and food intake. A lot of roughage and fibre in the diet is essential for adequate evacuation of bowels.

To prevent or cure constipation, food rich in soluble and insoluble fibre or roughage must be consumed. This consists mainly of fruit and vegetables (which provide insoluble fibre) and wholegrain cereals and pulses (which provide soluble fibre). Roughage stimulates bowel action and removes accumulated waste from the intestines. Lots of mineral water (i.e., organic water of fruit and vegetables) and ordinary water must be drunk to remove excess heat and prevent the dehydration of stools.

Recommended Food

Fruit: Banana, apricot, pineapple, jackfruit and apple (contains cellulose and pectin fibres, the former acting only as roughage and the latter absorbing water, add bulk to waste matter, facilitating an easy and early evacuation of bowels and relieving the intestinal mucous lining from harmful bacteria); ripe bael in the form of sherbet with jaggery (cleans and tones up intestines and cools the system); fresh or dried figs (due to the high cellulose content in the skin and the seeds, which are very large in number and stimulate the peristaltic movement of the intestines). Dried figs should be soaked in water overnight and taken in the morning along with the water. Dried dates and raisins are also best eaten this way. Guava, orange and ripe papaya should be taken as the first and only thing for breakfast in the morning. Grapes purify blood and stimulate the activity of bowels and kidneys); Indian gooseberry, mango, pear and jambul fruit.

Vegetables: Bottle gourd, cabbage, cucumber, spinach, carrot, parwal, goosefoot white, radish, green leafy vegetables, snake gourd, pumpkin and tomato. The banana flower and its inner stem are rich in fibre. Raw potato juice, as well as the juice of all the above-mentioned vegetables in their raw state, are rich in mineral water. Whole vegetables as salads are ideal for their roughage content.

Other items: Wholewheat flour or wheat, rice bran, lemon juice with warm water (to be taken on an empty stomach in the morning, and a few times during the day); sesame seed, sprouts and chapatis made from whole flour of cereals and wholegrain pulses.

DIABETES

An endocrine disorder of the pancreas gland, diabetes indicates that the body is deficient in insulin and is unable to burn up or utilise sugar either in its food intake or in the sugar stored in the body in complex forms such as starches. As a result, sugar accumulates in the blood and is passed in the urine. Patients feel unusually thirsty, pass urine frequently and lose weight in spite of an increased appetite. Tiredness, drowsiness, itching, boils, dry skin, slow healing of wounds, fungal infections of mouth, tongue and vagina are the other symptoms.

Diabetes is passed on from one generation to the next. Excessive use of white, refined sugar, non-vegetarian food, fried, spicy, refined food and sweets may be the cause of diabetes. Overeating, obesity and lack of physical exercise may also lead to this disease. Diabetes is also associated with other diseases like hypothyroidism, liver diseases, cortisone or steroid excesses and chronic alcoholism.

Daily exercise with a suitable diet is necessary, because utilisation of simple carbohydrates occurs in the presence of oxygen. Blood sugar levels rise in the absence of even simple exercise such as walking.

Diabetes is essentially due to insufficient or inadequate production of insulin by the pancreas as per the amount of carbohydrate consumed. Carbohydrate is either consumed in its simple forms like glucose, fructose and maltose or in its complex forms such as starches and sugars. Insulin is a secretion of the pancreatic gland that helps to metabolise carbohydrates (simple or complex) in the body. When more carbohydrates than the body can metabolise completely into carbon dioxide, water and energy are consumed, the overburdened pancreas is unable to produce the required amount of insulin. The products of incomplete metabolism are simpler sugars like maltose and glucose. These accumulate in the blood as blood sugar.

To prevent and cure diabetes, food containing insulin (e.g. sprouted grains) or an insulin-like active principle (e.g. bitter gourd) should be eaten; compensate or supply the deficiency by eating foods that stimulate the production of insulin (e.g. French beans); cut down the body's requirement of insulin by reducing the consumption of carbohydrates, especially starches and sugars; provide a sufficient supply of vitamins (especially C and A) and minerals, which are essential for the pancreas; and ensure a high fibre diet: the soluble fibre in fruit, currants, barley and soyabeans is very helpful in reducing blood sugar levels.

Recommended Food

Fruit: Jambul (fresh fruit or dried and powdered), almond, grape, lemon.

Vegetables: Bitter gourd is essential because it contains an insulin-like active principle. It must be eaten daily either powdered or as juice. Bitter gourd also contains lots of minerals, which help in preventing neuritis, hypertension and eye complications. Its regular use increases the body's resistance to infections during diabetes. It also helps in controlling excessive thirst and thus prevents a loss of sodium through sweating and urination. Soyabean contains a large amount of protein and little starch, and is eminently suitable. It can be used in many forms such as soyamilk, soyabean chunks, soyabean sprouts and soyabean powder.

Lettuce, tomato and turnip are very low in carbohydrates and provide plenty of minerals. Tomato also helps in controlling the sugar levels in the blood.

Carrot contains a hormone known as tocokinin, which is an insulin-like compound, so it is very good for diabetics, as are French beans and string beans. Their juice stimulates the production of insulin.

Other vegetables like cucumber, spinach, cabbage, curry leaves, fenugreek leaves and almond are all very useful for diabetics. Unripe banana, cooked as a vegetable, is also very good.

Other items: Onion juice, fenugreek, lemons, dried tender mango leaves, bael-leaf juice or dhruva-grass juice. Sprouted pulses and cereals such as green gram, Bengal gram and black gram are very helpful in lowering blood sugar and preventing complications due to malnutrition.

DIARRHEA AND DYSENTERY

Diarrhoea and dysentery may be due to indigestion, inflammatory conditions of the alimentary canal and disorders of absorption, secretion or digestion. Chronic intestinal infections may be due to bacterial or parasitic agents like salmonella, streptococci, fungi, amoebae, viruses and giardia. They may also be due to some organic or chronic diseases like intestinal tumours, tuberculosis of the intestine and laxative abuses.

Diarrhoea and dysentery are accompanied by the urgent desire to evacuate the bowels, either just after eating meals or during the night. They may be associated with fever, loss of weight, abdominal pain, distention and with tenesmus (ineffectual and painful straining while urinating or passing stools) of the rectum.

They are essentially due to an inflammation of the alimentary canal as a result of the acidic decomposition of putrefying food (due to indigestion, food poisoning, etc.) and bacilli (as in tuberculosis of the intestines).

To prevent and cure diarrhoea or dysentery, it is necessary to reduce or soothe the inflammation by drinking cucumber, carrot, beetroot and ash gourd juice, which have alkaline and mineral properties; constipating but easily digestible positive food should be eaten, like apple, pomegranate, banana or ripe banana soup; check or kill the harmful bacteria by giving antibacterial, antifungal natural food like mint and garlic; and replace the loss of water and important alkaline salts by drinking coconut water, whey of milk, lassi or diluted, salted buttermilk, pomegranate or other fruit juice and vegetable soup.

Food with fibre, e.g., green leafy vegetables, should be avoided as it may irritate the already inflamed alimentary canal. Acid-producing food, that is foods which have acidic end products like proteins, starches, fats and carbohydrates should also be avoided.

Recommended Food

Fruit: Apple, which has a binding effect because it contains pectin. Pectin forms a gelatin which dissolves the toxic poisons in the intestines and checks diarrhoea. Bael fruit (fresh or dried) is good becaue it contains tannin and is good for dysentery with mucous, and pain in the stomach accompanied by blood in the faeces.

Pomegranate skin infusions or fresh pomegranate juice is also very helpful.

Banana (which changes intestinal flora from harmful bacilli to beneficial bacilli), either whole or as a soup is beneficial. Jambul, orange and plum are good, and so is Indian gooseberry mixed with lemon juice and sugar candy.

Vegetables: Gourds and potatoes in their well-cooked form; carrot (as a good source of pectin, it prevents the inflammation of the intestine and supplies sodium, potassium, phosphorus, sulphur, magnesium and calcium, which prevent dehydration, to the body). Carrot can be taken as juice, as soup or in any cooked form. Beetroot should be taken as a juice or soup, pumpkin is good, either as soup or boiled. It has very few calories, but supplies plenty of vitamins and minerals.

Other items: Coconut water (since it checks dehydration and supplies potassium salts; 1 tablespoon every ten minutes, especially coconut water mixed with a little lemon juice); garlic (as it brings down the inflammation of the intestines and kills bacteria/worms, especially in persistent diarrhoea); whey of milk (contains little proteins, fats and carbohydrates, but supplies a good amount of minerals); buttermilk preferably alone or with a little rice (as it has a cooling effect; the lactic acid bacilli also kill the germs of diarrhoea and dysentery); mint juice with lemon and honey, cumin, basil leaves with sugar, decoction of coriander or aniseed with black salt, roasted aniseed with sugar candy and lemon juice in warm water 3–4 times a day, onion with curd, and fenugreek seeds ground with curd.

DISORDER OF THE PROSTATE GLAND

Enlargement of the prostate gland is very common in men over the age of sixty. Frequent urination, dribbling of urine, headache, nervousness, irritability and general weakness are the early symptoms of prostate enlargement.

The patient feels very uncomfortable while passing urine, feels the urge to urinate several times even at night and needs effort to empty the bladder. Retention of urine may lead to cystitis and other kidney diseases.

To prevent and cure this disorder, the enlarged prostate gland has to be brought down to normal size by supplying the system with iodine. Food containing iodine must therefore be consumed. Potassium-and-zinc-rich food also helps. It provides the system with the minerals that are so essential for curing this ailment.

Recommended Food

Fruit: Apple, bael, cherry and peach.

Vegetables: Cabbage, carrot, drumstick, brinjal, bottle gourd, ash gourd with its seeds (contain protein and non-coagulating fats, potassium and zinc), cucumber, amaranth, spinach and yam.

Other items: Pumpkin, sunflower and sesame seed, linseed and groundnut.

Avoid potato, red chilli, radish, pepper and anything which is sour and can cause irritation.

EYE DISEASES

Conjunctivitis, trachoma, cataract and night-blindness are common eye diseases. Conjunctivitis may be due to a bacterial or viral infection. Itching, redness, swelling and watering of the eyes are common symptoms, and may be due to malnutrition, heredity or injury.

The essential cause of these defects is lack of vitamin A or its precursor, and vitamin C, which is always needed for the repair or cure of any organ in the body.

To prevent and cure eye disorders, supply the body with large doses of vitamins A and C to make up any deficiency. Both these vitamins fight against bacterial or viral infections, and help to repair any injury.

Recommended Food

Fruit: Fruit rich in vitamins A and C include: Indian gooseberry (which is the richest source of vitamin C; its juice mixed with honey is ideal for glaucoma and conjunctivitis), apple, orange (vitamin C), papaya, mango (vitamin A—acts as an eye tonic, cures night-blindness, itching and blurring in the eyes), tomato (vitamin A and other minerals) and water melon.

Vegetables: Pumpkin, carrot, spinach, tomato, green peas, cucumber, gourds, beans, onion, turnip and cabbage (especially the outer leaves).

Other items: Honey, cumin seed with curd, melon seed and sprouted cereal.

HEADACHE AND MIGRAINE

Headaches, may be caused by injury, intracranial-like meningitis, vascular-like hypertension, cough, systemic causes resulting from carbon monoxide or carbon dioxide poisoning, hypoglycemia, fevers, constipation and overexertion, or because of ailments of ears, teeth and eyes.

Migraine, or recurrent headaches which is unilateral either on the right or left side of the head, may be associated with nausea, vomiting and vertigo.

The essential cause of headache and migraine is the lack of a sufficient amount of vitamins A, B and C, and minerals that combat or deal with the toxic causes of headaches (like fevers), constipation, poisoning (by carbon monoxide or carbon dioxide gases) or physiological imbalances due to overexertion, the heat of the sun and loss of sleep. For example, overexertion, tension or an upset could result in the body not being able to properly digest food. Fermentation and gas formation as a result of this metabolic imbalance, leads to a headache. Highly alkaline mineral salts and fibre help to neutralise the acidic conditions arising from internal or external causes, for example, by aiding in bowel movement, for example, one of the internal causes is removed.

To prevent and cure headache and migraine, stop or prevent any acidity or toxicity from forming due to the above-mentioned causes by not eating when tired so as to prevent constipation. Avoid external causes like exposure to too much sun and carbon monoxide poisoning. Provide the system with highly alkaline and vitamin-rich food that will help neutralise these causes. Avoid excessive salt.

Recommended Foods

Fruit: Apple, ripe grapes, Indian gooseberry, fig, pomegranate and guava.

Vegetables: Radish and its leaves; other green leafy vegetables like coriander, amaranth, fenugreek leaves and goose foot white; cucumber, tomato and cabbage.

Other items: Ginger, almond (rich in vitamin B and niacin) and groundnut.

HEART AILMENTS

Heart ailments include hypertension, arteriosclerosis (degeneration of the arteries), heart attack and angina. Hypertension is one of the commonest diseases nowadays. Blood pressure above 140/90 mm Hg is considered high. Hypertension can be termed as primary when there is no obvious causal factor, and secondary when there is some identifiable cause. Primary hypertension may be due to genetic factors, chronic stress, excessive salt in the diet, an excessive intake of alcohol, smoking and obesity. Secondary hypertension may be due to renal diseases (hydronephrosis, enlarged prostate), hormonal disorders (hypo/hyperthyroidism), head injury, encephalitis, pregnancy toxemia or oral contraceptives. The main symptom of hypertension is the presence of a headache on waking up.

Other heart diseases like arteriosclerosis (hardening of the blood vessels), angina pectoris and myocardial infarction may be due to heredity, high dietary intake of fats, cholesterol and sugar, hypertension, obesity, emotional factors (like aggressiveness) and diabetes mellitus. Besides these, some of the other major risk factors are smoking, alcoholism, chronic blood pressure and high blood cholesterol level. The main symptoms are pain in the chest, left arm or both arms, difficulty in breathing, a choking sensation in throat, fainting, nausea and sweating.

Heart ailments are essentially due to cholesterol accumulating in blood vessels and causing the hardening of arteries and veins. This hardening reduces the diameter of the blood vessels, and hampers the flow of blood. Heart ailments are also due to vitamin B deficiency.

To treat and prevent heart ailments, food that is low in cholesterol, and that dissolves the deposits of calcium and cholesterol in the blood vessels should be taken. The already-existing high levels of cholesterol must be brought down by a restricted diet and other methods.

Recommended Food

Fruit: Apple, rich in sodium and vitamins A, B^1, B^2, B^6 and C helps in the prevention and treatment of heart diseases. Grapes are thought to be a heart tonic, effective in reducing heart pain and palpitation. Dates and Indian gooseberry strengthen the heart. Orange juice with honey is highly beneficial in conditions like coronary ischemia and myocardial infarction, when a purely liquid diet is advisable. Pectin found in the peel and rind of citrus fruit (grapes and oranges) helps to lower blood cholesterol. Bananas contain potassium which helps in lowering high blood pressure. Pineapples, melon seeds, papayas (due to the enzyme papain) and pomegranates are also beneficial.

Vegetables: Raw beetroot and its juice help in dissolving inorganic calcium deposits. Carrot is a good source of alkaline elements, which revitalise the blood and nourish the entire system. Pumpkin and mint are very good as are snake gourd, beans and cucumber.

Other items: Lemon is a good source of vitamin C, and is beneficial for high blood pressure and arteriosclerosis. It also strengthens the heart and the entire arterial system. Garlic, raw or cooked, has the power to slow the pulse, modify heart rhythm, widen blood vessels and control dizziness and shortness of breath. It often helps in preventing heart attacks and in reducing cholesterol levels. Onion is very efficient in controlling heart diseases since it contains a number of useful oils, catechol, protocatechuic acid, thiocyanate, calcium, phosphorus, iron and other vitamins, which help in thinning the blood, preventing thrombosis and reducing blood cholesterol. Honey contains acetylcholine, which helps in lowering high blood pressure and controlling the heart rate. Coconut water strengthens the heart. Indian gooseberry, peepal, alfa-alfa (greens of alfa-alfa seeds or the seeds themselves), basil and coriander seed are also helpful.

Salt, alcohol, non-vegetarian food, smoking and fats should be avoided. Yogasanas especially shavasana should be practiced.

HYPERACIDITY AND PEPTIC ULCERS

Hyperacidity results from poor food habits, such as excessive intake of refined, fatty, fried, spicy and starchy food. The fermentation of such food in the stomach causes hyperacidity. Hyperacidity in the stomach coupled with tension, frustration, worry and stress, increase the excessive formation of acids in the stomach. This results in ulcers. The symptoms include a burning sensation in the chest due to reflux of acid, belching, stomach pain, loss of appetite, nausea and vomiting. In the case of duodenal ulcers, pain occurs 2–3 hours after a meal, and is eased by an intake of food. The pain is invariably absent in the mornings. In the case of gastric ulcers pain after eating and anaemia are prominent symptoms.

The pain is essentially due to a burning feeling caused by (a) excessive secretion of hydrochloric acid in the stomach which adversely affects (sours) the mucous membrane of the stomach; (b) the highly acidic nature of the decomposition (or end-products, including gases) of improper or incomplete digestion (or metabolism) of fatty, starchy and proteinaceous foods. Such acidic end-products irritate and corrode the delicate mucous lining of the stomach, causing ulcers. These acidic end-products also destroy cells and tissues; (c) intake of very spicy and oily foods; (d) inadequate consumption of enough fruit, vegetables and fibrous foods. A proper diet supplying food rich in minerals and vitamins can go a long way in minimising the ill-effects of stress.

Prevention and cure: (a) nullify the excess hydrochloric acid or acidic end-products by various means such as providing the system with plenty of alkaline foods containing organic minerals and vitamins, such as fruit and vegetables; (b) help the the body to stop the production of excess hydrochloric acid or acidic end-products of metabolism by avoiding excessive intake of proteins, starches, fats, carbohydrates, spicy food, alcohol and smoking. All this kind of food must be drastically cut down; (c) tone up the digestive system by a proper and sufficient intake of fruit and vegetables, and exercise; (d) avoid eating heavy foods when upset, tense, tired, or under other negative emotions. At such times, the production of enzymes and hormones is insufficient and defective. As a result digestion becomes inefficient and slows down, leading to improper, incomplete digestion, which in turn results in acidity and associated problems.

Recommended Food

Fruit: Grapefruit contains citric acid, which is oxidised within the body and hence increases the alkalinity of body fluids. Cooked rice with milk and banana relieves acidity in the stomach.

Vegetables: Raw green banana and its flower thicken the lining of the stomach and prevent harmful secretions. They also help in healing gastric ulcers. Potato and cabbage are very effective, especially, the juice of raw potato or cabbage which acts as a medicine and cures acidity and ulcers fast. Potato starch is anti-inflammatory in the case of gastro-intestinal ailments. Cabbage juice is very effective in curing duodenal ulcers. Two to four tablespoons of cabbage juice daily with a natural balanced diet are advised. Cabbage juice can be made palatable by adding honey or pineapple or lemon juice. Carrot too can treat ulcers and regular use even prevents gastric ulcers. Cucumber juice (one cup taken every six hours) is a useful remedy. It gives immediate relief from acidity. Lady's fingers are useful in the treatment of gastric ulcers. Bitter gourd and spinach are also very effective. Cooked radish and its juice (with sugar added) provides relief from acidity.

Other items: Coconut is very effective in the treatment of acidity as its oil reduces the acid secretion of the stomach. Dried coconut can decrease excess acid secretion in the stomach and help cure the symptoms caused by excessive acid. Onion, lemon and honey are also helpful. Sucking on a clove after a meal can prevent hyperacidity.

INDIGESTION AND FLATULENCE

The symptoms of indigestion are stomachache, loss of appetite, vomiting, the bloating of the stomach and irregular motions. It is essentially due to overeating, irregular eating, eating too often (eating a meal before the previous meal has been digested), eating contaminated and spoilt food, stress, lack of sleep, over-exertion and organic diseases like tuberculosis and anaemia, diseases of the gall bladder, pancreas and intestinal worms. Flatulence is due to bacterial fermentation and enzymatic action on the undigested food leading to the formation of gas. Gas produced from decomposition is normally acidic.

To prevent and cure indigestion and flatulence, the existing conditions of the same must be dealt with first, and the causes eliminated. Eat only easily digestible food like fruit and vegetables. Avoid eating too frequently. Do not eat heavy food when tense, depressed, sleepless or over-worked etc. At such times eat a very light meal of vegetables/fruit, soup or juice since the process of digestion slows down and there is improper and insufficient secretion of enzymes and digestive juices. This leads to poor digestion which causes the formation of gas.

Recommended Food

Fruit: Papaya is very beneficial as it contains an enzyme (papain) which helps digestion. Figs also contain an enzyme, ficin, which aids digestion. Pineapple contains an enzyme called biosmelin which resembles pepsin and therefore helps to digest food. Apple, banana pith juice, jambul juice, orange juice, water melon and mango are also effective.

Vegetables: Carrot juice with honey is a good therapy for indigestion and flatulence. Brinjal is also very useful. Carrot checks the growth of harmful bacteria in the intestines and prevents vomiting, and supplies lots of minerals and pectin, which coat the intestines to allay inflammation. For morning sickness and colic caused by indigestion, mint juice combined with lemon juice and honey is very effective. Cucumber, tomato juice and radish and its tender leaves are very useful. A blend of carrot, beetroot and spinach juice is very beneficial.

Other items: Indian gooseberry, garlic and onion juice are effective. The juice of one lemon in one glass of warm water should be taken on an empty stomach in the morning. Lime juice stimulates the secretion of saliva in the mouth and other digestive enzymes in the digestive canal promoting the process of digestion. Ginger juice taken half an hour before meals is good for preventing indigestion. Ginger is very effective especially when its juice is taken in combination with the juices of mint and lemon, and honey. It can also be taken in the form of a decoction. Thyme and black salt in warm water, and asafoetida and turmeric are very useful remedies.

INTESTINAL WORMS

In India, the most common parasites of the human intestine are tapeworms, roundworms, hookworms and whipworms. Common symptoms include discomfort in the abdomen, excessive hunger and loss of weight. Worms may come out of the anus spontaneously or in stools. A generalised skin rash, anaemia, palpitation, physical and mental tiredness may be seen in case of hook worms. Whip worm infection may affect the growth of children. These infections generally enter the body when larvae are swallowed, usually in contaminated food or by contact with infected faeces as the larvae of hook worms penetrate the skin. Taenia solium infection is caused by eating infected pork.

It is essentially the presence of the morbid wastes of metabolism in the intestines which provide the right conditions for the entry, production and growth of worms or their larvae. The accidental entry of these larvae into the body can be tackled by the body if the immune system is competent and is rich in organic minerals and vitamins.

In order to cure and prevent intestinal worms, the existing larvae or their worms must be expelled or killed, further entry of these into the body must be prevented and an anti-worm medium (i.e., good internal hygiene) must be introduced or built-up in the body by the intake of antibacterial food, and plenty of fruit and vegetables. Tender banana stem preparations are also effective.

Recommended Food

Fruit: Papaya contains the enzyme papain which is effective in eliminating worms. The milky juice of unripe papaya can destroy roundworms. Papaya juice can be taken with honey. Papaya seeds are also very effective in expelling roundworms as they contain a powerful substance called caricin. Papaya leaves contain carpaine and can expel intestinal worms. Pineapple juice, mango, orange and apple are also beneficial. The bark of the pomegranate tree is very effective for killing intestinal worms. It can be taken as a decoction to expel tapeworms.

Vegetables: Mint juice is very effective in expelling thread worms when taken with lime juice and honey. Carrot is very useful for eliminating threadworms and other parasites. Take raw grated carrot as breakfast every morning. Gourd and pumpkin seeds are also very effective in expelling intestinal worms. Bitter gourd juice, pumpkin juice, fenugreek-mint juice and snake gourd are very beneficial.

Other items: Garlic is excellent for expelling worms. It can destroy harmful bacteria in the intestine without affecting beneficial organisms. It can be eaten in any form or with currant in the form of a paste. Garlic juice can be taken with a glass of warm water and a tablespoon of onion juice. Coconut is a time-tested and very effective remedy for eliminating intestinal worms of all kinds. Ginger juice has purgative properties, so it destroys intestinal worms which are then excreted through faeces. Lemon, basil, bael leaves, neem leaves, asafoetida, turmeric and thyme are also effective remedies. Asafoetida and thyme when taken together are a good medicine for expelling worms. Tomato juice and walnuts are also very effective in dealing with intestinal worms.

JAUNDICE AND HEPATITIS

Jaundice is the result of increased levels of bile in the blood. This may be due to an obstruction of the flow of bile from the liver or may be due to hepatitis A, B or C, or increased destruction of blood cells. This condition gives the eyes and the skin a yellow colouration. It destroy liver tissues, the extent depending on the severity of the disease. The cause of infectious hepatitis may be viral, bacterial or protozoal. The direct causes are alcohol, pneumonia, malaria or burns. The main symptoms are yellowness of the eyes and skin, loss of appetite, clay-coloured faeces, dark yellow urine, nausea, vomiting and pain in the abdomen.

It is essentially due to a malfunctioning of the liver leading to an increase of the bile content in the blood. Liver tissues are destroyed to a great extent.

In order to treat and prevent jaundice and hepatitis, food high in potassium and low in albumin and sodium should be taken.

Recommended Food

Fruit: Papaya is very helpful in jaundice and can be taken in the form of a curry. It ensures the efficient working of the liver. Mineral rich watermelon and its seeds are very effective in liver ailments. Musk melon seeds are also very useful in jaundice. Figs and grapes because they contain a large amount of potassium, and are low in albumin and sodium, induce the elimination of waste and morbid matter from the body. Pomegranate juice, ripe mango, sugarcane (chewed raw), figs, orange, apple and pineapple are also good for liver disorders. A mixture of juice of papaya (invigorates the liver), fresh turmeric, grapes, orange and sweet lime is very good. Jambul fruit activates the liver and acts as a tonic fot it.

Vegetables: The juice of radish leaves is highly valuable for the treatment of jaundice. It can be sweetened by adding glucose. The high amount of protein, calcium, sodium and other minerals it contains are responsible for curing jaundice, inducing appetite and evacuation of bowels. Tomato juice is very effective in the treatment of jaundice and hepatitis. Beetroot contains potassium and sodium which help to cleanse the liver and kidneys. A mixture of tomato and carrot juice induces the formation of red blood cells and acts as a good liver tonic. Bitter gourd juice should be taken on an empty stomach. Bottle gourd, mint, parwal, radish and cucumber are also beneficial. Soak two tablespoons of grated radish with two tablespoons of sugar candy overnight, and take on an empty stomach.

Other items: Indian gooseberry juice is very good for liver disorders. Rice has no fibre content and therefore soothes the digestive system during hepatitis and jaundice. Coconut water acts as a natural diuretic in liver ailments. The lactic acid organisms in curd prevent the formation of ammonia (free ammonia is one of the major causes of coma in hepatitis). Buttermilk or curd with honey is an ideal diet in liver ailments. Fenugreek leaves contain sulphur and chlorine which clean the liver and rejuvenate it. The germicidal and disinfectant properties of garlic or its juice help in destroying intestinal bacteria. Indian gooseberry, black currant and raisins are beneficial during liver disorders. The juice of fresh turmeric is also very good as it vitalises and stimulates the liver. Fresh sugarcane juice is very beneficial in jaundice.

MENSTRUAL IRREGULARITIES

The menstrual cycle which is usually of 26 to 32 days may be shortened or extended. Menstruation may be associated with headache, excessive pain in the lower abdomen, backache, pain in the legs and sometimes vomiting. Excessive bleeding may lead to other complications like anaemia or debility. Insufficient bleeding may also occur.

Menstrual disorders are essentially due to a malfunctioning of the reproductive system due to factors like accumulation of toxic matter, injury or infection.

In order to cure and prevent such disorders the reproductive organ must be given the proper nourishment to ensure that it functions properly thereby assisting in regular and proper menstrual cycle/flow.

Recommended Food

Fruit: Grapes and pineapple are very useful for regulating the menstrual cycle. Unripe papaya helps in the contraction of uterine muscles ensuring proper menstrual flow. It is very beneficial in the case of delayed menstruation due to exposure to cold or due to fear.

Vegetables: Carrot juice is valuable for regulating the menstrual cycle. The mixed juice of leafy vegetables is also very good for treating menstrual disorders. Amaranth green and beetroot are useful in all types of bleeding including excessive menstruation. Cooked banana flower with curd is a good remedy for menstrual disorders like painful menstruation and excessive bleeding.

Other items: Ginger is very useful specially in delayed menstruation. Groundnuts are beneficial in excessive bleeding. Sesame seed taken with hot water two days prior to the expected date are very effective in reducing pain during menstruation and for curing scanty menstruation. Thyme seed, cumin seed, aniseed with jaggery and parsley are helpful in regulating menstruation.

OBESITY

Normal body weight varies according to age, sex and height. Obesity or being overweight is a condition in which the body weight increases by 20 per cent or more of the normal range, due to the excessive deposition of fatty tissues. The main causes of simple obesity are genetic, overeating due to food addiction, psychiatric illness, hypoglycemic syndrome, peptic ulcers and lack of exercise. Sometimes obesity also accompanies other disorders like adiposity, pregnancy close to menopause, hypothyroidism, disorders of the pancreas and cerebral injuries. Obesity may lead to many harmful conditions like hypertension, ankle edema, coronary heart disease, varicose veins, mental disturbance, gall bladder disease, osteoarthritis, back pain, non-insulin-dependent diabetes, menstrual irregularities and impotence. There should be a balance between the physical activities and the food intake of an individual.

Obesity is essentially due to a high calorie and low fibre diet, consumption of food in excess of body requirements and physical needs for long periods of time. The quality and quantity of food needed varies from person to person.

In order to prevent obesity, a low-calorie and high-fibre diet should be taken. A diet consisting of low amounts of fat, sugar and salt along with an intake of plenty of water helps in reducing body weight. The existing excessive fat must be got rid of through diet and exercise and further build up of fat must be stopped. A low fat diet alone will not be very effective. It should be coupled with a high fibre diet. Whatever the diet, it should be closely monitored by a physician. This is particularly true for those with disorders such as heart disease or diabetes.

Recommended Food

Fruit: A banana diet with its low fat content is considered good for obese people. Banana is very rich in potassium and has no sodium and is therefore most suitable for overweight people. A diet containing four to six bananas and four glasses of skimmed milk is given to overweight people during the course of weight reduction. Pineapple, grapefruit, melon, orange, cherry and watermelon are very effective for weight reduction.

Vegetables: Cabbage contains tartonic acid which prevents the formation of fats from excess sugar and starches in the body. About 100 grams of cabbage contains only 27 calories and a significant amount of calcium, phosphorus and vitamin C. Tomato is very low in carbohydrates and is considered very effective in reducing body weight when taken early in the morning in place of breakfast for 2–3 months. Cucumber, gourds and green leafy vegetables like coriander, goosefoot white and fenugreek are very effective food remedies.

Other items: Indian gooseberry and thyme help in weight reduction. Lemon juice and honey in warm water on an empty stomach is very effective. It has a calming effect on nerves. Regular use can cause weight loss in 2–3 months. Fasting with lemon juice and water is also advisable in acute cases for some days but should be done under the supervision of a naturopath.

TOOTH DECAY AND CARIES

Tooth decay, caries and pyorrhoea are generally associated with the deficiency of vitamins A, C, D, phosphorus and calcium. Overindulgence in sweets, acidic condition of stomach and food particles lodged between the teeth cause decay. Generally, tooth decay is seen in children who eat too many chocolates and sweets. This is because a child's system requires calcium for digestion, and when sufficient calcium is not available, it is 'sucked' from teeth and bones. This is why children in particular should have a calcium-rich diet. A balanced diet and proper dental hygiene should be maintained by brushing teeth after each meal so as to prevent the growth of harmful bacteria and remove decayed food particles.

Very hot or very cold water/food destroys the enamel of teeth thus making them sensitive.

In order to prevent tooth decay and caries, calcium-rich foods should be eaten. Chocolates and sweets should be avoided. Proper dental hygiene should be maintained by brushing teeth after each meal. Vitamins A and C in large amounts must be supplied to the body. Indian gooseberry, carrot, papaya and green leafy vegetables are ideal. Food particles should not be allowed to lodge in the mouth between the teeth.

Recommended Food

Fruit: Vitamin C and calcium-rich lemon, orange and grapefruit are very effective in curing and preventing dental caries, pyorrhea and other tooth ailments. Powdered dry rind of pomegranate mixed with salt and applied on teeth as tooth powder strengthens the gums, prevents bleeding gums and pyorrhea. Apple prevents tooth decay. Regularly eating an apple after a meal helps in cleaning the teeth properly and its acid content helps in destroying harmful bacterial growth. Therefore it is regarded as a safeguard against all tooth ailments.

Vegetables: Chewing onion and carrot destroy harmful bacteria in the mouth, cleanse the mouth, prevent bleeding gums and tooth decay. Mint is a good tooth tonic and has antiseptic properties. It kills the harmful bacteria causing bad odour and keeps the mouth fresh. Spinach and spinach juice are very effective in curing bleeding gums and dental cavities. Curry leaves are also very helpful.

Other items: Groundnuts are good for strengthening gums and tooth enamel. Honey has mild antiseptic properties and helps prevent bacterial growth. It is a very good tonic for teeth and prevents decay and early loss of teeth. Indian gooseberry, clove and lemon are also very beneficial.

URINARY DISORDERS

These include glomerulonephritis, pyelonephritis, nephrotic syndrome, asymptomatic haematuria (blood in urine) and proteinuria (protein in urine), urinary tract infection (UTI) and urinary stones. Of these, urinary tract infection is very common. Symptoms include sudden onset of fever with rigor, weakness, nausea, vomiting, pain in the lower abdomen, painful and frequent urination (sometimes with blood). It may be associated with pregnancy, absence of complete emptying of bladder, stones, unhygienic sexual intercourse or diabetes mellitus. Nephrotic syndrome is a clinical condition in which there is swelling of the body. Blood and proteins are present in urine. It is more common in childhood. Swelling of the body (in particular the lower limbs), loss of appetite, diarrhoea, vomiting, tiredness and high blood pressure are the main symptoms. In these diseases, significant water intake, and a high protein and low sodium diet are important for both prevention and treatment.

Recommended Food

Fruit: Banana stem juice, figs, musk melon, water melon, grapes and papaya are very good. Pineapple juice stimulates the activity of the kidneys and helps to remove toxic elements and waste products from the body.

Vegetables: Carrot juice and cucumber are good diuretics. Lettuce and lady's fingers are effective in treating urinary disorders. Juice of banana stem improves the functional efficiency of kidneys by helping in the elimination of toxins and removal of stones in the kidneys. Spinach juice is beneficial in nephritis, cystitis, frequent urination and high acidity of urine. Tomato is highly alkaline in nature and contain vitamins A and C and helps prevent recurrent urinary tract infection. Bottle gourd is cooling, alkaline and diuretic in nature, and helps cure painful and burning urination. Cucumber and its seeds have potassium which is useful in reducing hyperacidity in urine. Onion is very effective when there is retention of urine and burning urination. Ash gourd juice is also very helpful.

Other items: Coconut water, Indian gooseberry juice and jambul are diuretics. Saffron and lemon are also beneficial.

6

Methods of Cooking

The various methods of cooking are (1) baking, (2) boiling, (3) frying (shallow and deep), (4) roasting, (5) steaming and (6) stewing. Baking, boiling, steaming and simmering are conservative ways of cooking. Cooking on high heat initially till the vegetable is heated and then on low heat till cooked is believed to retain the nutrients.

I. BAKING

In this method, food is cooked by dry heat in a closed container at a very high temperature. Normally baking soda or baking powder is used when baking; this destroys vitamins, especially vitamin B, and leaves an alkaline ash of sodium carbonate. Instead, ammonium carbonate may be used, which gives ammonia and carbon dioxide gases that escape without leaving an alkaline or acidic inorganic residue.

2. BOILING

Food is cooked with water and brought to a boil. Use the minimum water possible. One way of doing this is to cook in a closed pan with a tight lid and keeping some cold water on the lid. When the hot steam formed inside the pan during boiling comes in contact with the lid, it gets cooled and condenses as liquid water into the vegetable and keeps it wet. Thus, the vegetable gets cooked with the minimum water and evaporation loss is also reduced. If required, add a little water to the vegetable while cooking.

First, boil the water and then add the vegetable to reduce contact of food with heat for a longer time. Cook in a closed pan to prevent oxidation. Do not throw away or drain the water in which vegetables are cooked or boiled. During boiling, water-soluble nutrients are drained into the water, especially from food containing vitamin B, vitamin C and mineral salts like sodium and potassium. If the water has to be drained, use it to (a) make the gravy for vegetable curries, (b) knead it with flour for chapatis or wheat dosas, (c) make a soup, sambar or rasam by adding a pinch of salt, a little lime juice, a little grated coconut, cut coriander leaves and spices (like mustard or cumin).

3. FRYING

In this process, foods are cooked in hot fat/oil. There are two types of frying: (a) shallow frying in which food is cooked by the heat provided by the hot oil and (b) deep frying.

In frying (shallow or deep), oil penetrates into the food making it difficult for digestive juices to penetrate the food. Both forms of frying entail an almost total loss of vitamins and other nutrients. Even the roughage or cellulose is lost. Thus fried food is very difficult to digest and taxes the digestive system.

It is, therefore, not advisable to adopt this method of cooking. If, however, food has to be fried occasionally, use a very small quantity of the oil or fat that is least harmful. The fats/oil should not be heated until it begins to 'smoke' This causes the compound choline to form, which produces a pungent smell in the food and also makes it difficult to digest.

Do not re-use oil which has already been used, even once, for deep frying. The decomposition products formed during the first frying will be decomposed further. The oil can however, be used for seasoning (where it is only mildly heated).

4. ROASTING

In this process, food is cooked in direct contact with the fire. The water content is thereby reduced, thus causing partial dehydration. The two disadvantages of this method are: (a) the skin becomes useless (because it is charred) and (b) vitamins and other nutrients are also lost, to a great extent, due to the excessive direct heat. It is believed that carbohydrates, when roasted, become easily digestible. However, due to loss of nutrients, the roasted product has lower nutritive value.

5. STEAMING

In this process, the food is cooked either by direct steam or by the heat of steam within a steam jacket. The food is placed on a perforated container over a pan of boiling water and gets cooked by steam coming through the pores of the container. In the case of a steam jacket, food is cooked in a bowl standing in a pan of constantly boiling water. This process of cooking is believed to retain the vitamins and minerals of the food to a great extent. Food may be steamed either in a closed pan at normal, or a little above normal pressure, or in a pressure cooker under higher pressure. The latter reduces the time taken, as well as exposure to air thereby minimising the loss of nutrients.

6. STEWING

The food is cooked by simmering (boiling gently) with water in a covered pan. This is better than boiling and food cooked this way is tastier and more easily digestible.

7

Common Recipes for Steamed/Boiled and Stuffed Vegetables

I. RECIPES FOR GRAVY (THIN/RAS) VEGETABLES

To prepare a vegetable with gravy, cook the vegetable ($\frac{1}{2}$ kg) with water (1–2 cups) and add this to any gravy. Enough water (or curd if it is a curd preparation) should be added to get the desired consistency of the vegetable.

Gravy Vegetable with Curd

(i) Kadi

Ingredients	Quantity
Bottle gourd/snake gourd/spinach/chow-chow etc.	(1" cubes) $\frac{1}{2}$ kg
Curd	2 cups
Water	2 cups
Bengal gram flour (preferably roasted)	$\frac{1}{2}$ cup
Turmeric powder	a pinch
Red chilli powder	$\frac{1}{2}$ tsp
Salt	to taste
Seasoning	
Ghee	$\frac{1}{2}$ tsp
Cumin	$\frac{1}{4}$ tsp
Asafoetida	a pinch
Red chilli powder (optional)	to taste

Method

1. Mix curd, water, Bengal gram flour, turmeric powder, red chilli powder and salt thoroughly.
2. Cook this in a pan till the gram flour is well cooked. Stir

frequently to avoid charring, adding more water/churned curd to get the desired consistency.

3. Season with cumin, asafoetida and red chilli powder.
4. Add the pre-cooked vegetables and mix well.

Optional: a) Add cabbage koftas (see Chapter 8) to the **kadi** and give one boil. b) Spoonfuls of pakoda batter with finely chopped onion/cabbage can be dropped into the hot boiling **kadi** and boiled till well-cooked. Do not stir or mix the pakodas until they are cooked, otherwise they may disintegrate.

(ii) Menthi Majjiga

Ingredients	Quantity
Spinach/bottle gourd/snake gourd/ cucumber/carrot (finely chopped)	½ kg
Curd/buttermilk	2 cups or more
Turmeric powder	a pinch
Salt	to taste
Coriander leaves (finely chopped)	1 tbsp
Beaten rice (optional)	½ cup
Seasoning	
Oil	½ tsp
Mustard	½ tsp
Cumin	¼ tsp
Asafoetida	a pinch
Thyme	½ tsp
Curry leaves	6–8
Green chilli	to taste

Method

1. To curd or buttermilk add turmeric powder, salt, coriander leaves, and a seasoning of mustard, cumin, asafoetida, thyme, curry leaves and chopped green chilli. Mix well.
2. Add any raw grated vegetable like cucumber, carrot, or cooked vegetable like spinach, bottle gourd, snake gourd or potato.
3. Beaten rice may also be added and allowed to soak for 30 minutes before serving.

(iii) Majjiga Pulusu (Moru Kozhambu)

Ingredients	Quantity
Spinach/bottle gourd/snake gourd/ chow-chow (1 cm cubes)	½ kg
Churned curd	2½ cups
Bengal gram flour or	2 tbsp
Split Bengal gram	2 tbsp
Rice	1 tbsp
Cumin (soaked and ground)	½ tsp
Green chilli	2
Fresh coconut (grated) (optional)	2 tbsp
Salt	to taste
Turmeric powder	¼ tsp
Water	1 cup
Seasoning	
Ghee	1 tsp
Black gram	1 tsp
Mustard	½ tsp
Asafoetida	a pinch
Red chilli	1
Curry leaves	6

Method

1. Churn the curd, either with just the Bengal gram flour, or with a paste of Bengal gram, rice, cumin, green chilli and salt. Add turmeric powder and water and boil till cooked.
2. Add the boiled vegetables and let the mixture come to a boil.
3. Season with black gram, mustard, asafoetida, red chilli and curry leaves.

For recipes: Using uncooked curd, see Raitas and Dips on pp. 246–48.

Gravy Vegetable with Pulses

Ingredients	Quantity
Any vegetable (finelychopped) including green leafy vegetables except starchy vegetables like yam, colocasia and potato	½ kg
Whole/split pulses	1 cup
water	2 cups

Method

1. Cook the pulses, vegetable and water together or separately, till the vegetable is well-cooked but not overcooked.
2. The most commonly used split pulses are red gram, Bengal gram, green gram, and lentils with or without skin. It is advisable to use pulses with skin and use whole pulses like whole green gram, black Bengal gram, matki and lentil. Sprouted pulses are very nutritions.

Any of the following seasonings can be added to the cooked vegetable:

(i) Simple seasoning of black gram (1 teaspoon, optional), mustard ($\frac{1}{2}$ teaspoon), asafoetida (a pinch) or garlic flakes (6, crushed), red chilli (to taste), curry leaves (6–8), onion and tomato (finely cut, $\frac{1}{4}$ cup each, both optional).

(ii) Kootu

Finely ground paste of fresh coconut (grated) (2 tbsp), green chilli (2), cumin ($\frac{1}{4}$ tsp) in addition to the seasoning. Add turmeric powder (a pinch) and heat till it boils.

(iii) With tomato

To cooked dal ($\frac{1}{2}$ cup red gram cooked in 1 cup water), add tomato ($\frac{1}{2}$" pieces, 1–2 cups depending upon the sourness of the tomato) and cook on low fire till the tomato is cooked. Then add the seasoning mentioned above, but without onions and tomato.

Gravy Vegetables without Pulses

(i) Gravy with Coriander Leaves, Onion and Tomato

Ingredients	Quantity
Any gourd (especially bottle gourd)/cabbage/ cauliflower/chow-chow/raw papaya (finely chopped)	$\frac{1}{2}$ kg.
Water	2 cups
Oil	1 tsp
Onion (finely chopped)	$\frac{1}{2}$ cup

Ingredients	Quantity
Coriander leaves (finely chopped)	1 cup
Tomato (finely chopped)	½ cup
Red chilli powder/green chilli paste	¼ tsp
Turmeric powder	a pinch
Salt	to taste
Maharashtrian kala masala powder	1 tsp
or	
Any masala powder	
Water	1 cup

Method

1. Cook the vegetable in water. Fry the pieces of onion. When fried, add coriander leaves.
2. Add tomato after a minute.
3. Fry on low fire for a minute or two, add red chilli powder or green chilli paste, turmeric powder, salt and if desired, a little masala powder or Maharashtrian kala masala powder or any other powder and water and boil.
4. Add the cooked vegetable, boil once and remove from fire.

(ii) Sweet and Sour Gravy (Pulusu)

Ingredients	Quantity
Tomato and onion/onion only/	(1 cm cubes) ½ kg
Green leafy vegetables/bottle gourd	
and pumkin/other vegetables	
Water	2 cups
Salt	to taste
Turmeric powder	a pinch
Green chilli	1 or 2
Thick tamarind extract	1 to 2 tbsp
Jaggery	1 big lime-sized ball
Tomato (optional)	1 or 2
Rice flour/Bengal gram flour	1 or 2 tsp ⎫ slurry
Water	2 tbsp ⎭
Seasoning	
Oil	1 tsp
Black gram	1 tsp
Mustard	½ tsp
Asafoetida	a pinch

Ingredients	Quantity
Red chilli	1 or 2
Curry leaves	6–8

Method

1. Boil vegetables in water.
2. Add salt, turmeric powder, green chilli, thick tamarind extract, jaggery, tomato and rice flour slurry to thicken the gravy and boil for a few minutes.
3. Season with black gram, mustard, asafoetida, red chilli and curry leaves.

Note: Instead of a slurry of flour, a little pre- cooked and partly mashed dal (e.g. red gram, green gram) or yam adds taste and flavour. The vegetables can also be mashed a little. A few coriander leaves may also be added while boiling.

If the peel of bottle gourd, or any other vegetable that is being used, has to be removed, then, grind the raw peel finely and cook along with the vegetable. The peel can also be cooked separately, then ground into a fine paste and added to the cooked curry. This way the gravy becomes thicker and the vegetable peel is also used.

The addition of sambar powder or pulusu powdhiye $\frac{1}{4}$ teaspoon of roasted mustard and roasted fenugreek powder (1:$\frac{1}{2}$ proportion) along with flour slurry adds flavour to the vegetable dish.

Water used to wash out remnants from a pan in which chutney or vegetable has been prepared could be added to the gravy to give it a special taste, flavour and blend.

The most commonly used vegetables are: i) Tomato and onion, in which case little or no tamarind is needed. ii) Small onion. iii) Green leafy vegetables like spinach, goosefoot white, colocasia leaves and onion leaves either individually or combined. iv) Bottle gourd and pumpkin. v) A variety of vegetables can be used in combination like brinjal, sweet potato, spring onion, raw papaya, chow-chow, cauliflower, cabbage and lady's fingers. However, when lady's fingers are used, they must be cooked with salt and tamarind. vi) The white portion of a water melon (after removing the red portion) can be cut into 1" or 1 cm cubes and used by itself or combined with other vegetables.

(iii) Aviyal with Coconut, Curd and Onion

Ingredients		Quantity
Beetroot alone or in combination with potato/ Beans/gourds (grated or thinly sliced)		½ kg
Water		½ cup
Onion (½" pieces)		½ cup
Fresh grated coconut	ground into a paste	2 tbsp
Green chillies		2
Sour/fresh curd		1 cup
Salt		to taste
Coconut oil		1 tsp
Curry leaves (chopped)		6–8

Method

1. Grind onion, coconut, green chilli and sour/fresh curd (or a little tamarind or raw mango, for sourness) into a paste.
2. Cook the vegetable, add salt, ground paste and mix well.
3. Add coconut oil and chopped curry leaves. Do not heat or boil after this.

(iv) Aviyal with Coconut and Green Chillies

Ingredients		Quantity
Drumstick (3" pieces)		12
Ash gourd		½ kg.
Pumpkin		¼ kg.
Drumstick	cut into 1" long strips	2
Yam		½ cup
Raw banana		½ cup
Snake gourd, beans, carrot		½ cup
Water		1 cup
Turmeric powder		a pinch
Salt		to taste
Fresh coconut (grated)		2–4 tbsp
Green chilli	ground into a paste	2
Cumin		¼ tsp
Fresh curd		2–4 tbsp

Ingredients	Quantity
Curry leaves (roughly chopped)	6
Coconut oil	1 tsp

Method

1. Grind coconut, green chillies, cumin, salt, sour or fresh curd and a little tamarind or mango for sourness (if desired) into a fine paste.
2. Cook vegetables in water. Add turmeric powder, salt and the paste. Mix well and remove from fire. 3. Add a few curry leaves and coconut oil. Cover with a lid. Do not heat or boil after this.

Notes: (i) If the aviyal is watery, sprinkle a teaspoon or two of rice or whole wheat flour, mix well immediately and cook for a minute or two.

(ii) When making **aviyal**, any vegetable except colocasia, lady's fingers, potato, onion and brinjal may be used.

(v) Aviyal/Curry with Fresh Coconut only

Ingredients		Quantity
Any vegetable (finely cut) other than lady's fingers, colocasia, potato, onion, Brinjal		½ kg
Water		1 cup or as per the consistency desired
Fresh coconut (grated)		2 tbsp
Salt	ground	to taste
Green chilli	into a paste	1 or 2
Cumin		½ tsp
Curry leaves		2–3
Coconut oil		1 tsp

Method

1. Boil the vegetable in water.
2. Add the paste of coconut, salt, green chillies and cumin.
3. Keep on fire for just a minute, remove from fire, add a few curry leaves and coconut oil.

(vi) Stew with Onion, Tomato and Flour

Ingredients	Quantity
A combination of all English vegetables:	
Beans	1 cup
Carrot } thin 2″ pieces	¼ cup
Capsicum	1 cup
Potato (½″ squares)	¼ cup
Cauliflower (florets)	a few
Cabbage (shredded)	2 cups
Green peas (shelled)	½ cup
Oil	1 tsp
Onion (1″ pieces)	1 cup
Whole wheat flour/rice flour	2 tsp
Tomato (1″ pieces)	1 or ½ cup
Salt	to taste
Water	1 cup
Pepper powder	1 tsp
Milk (optional)	½ cup
Fresh cream (optional)	1 tsp

Method

1. To hot oil, add onion, sprinkle a little water and fry/cook till half-done.
2. Add whole wheat flour (preferable) or rice flour and fry till the flour becomes slightly reddish.
3. Add tomato, keep for a while till tomato softens, add salt and water.
4. Cook the vegetables in water, add the above gravy and pepper powder. Boil twice.

Note: Instead of cooking vegetables in water and then adding the gravy, uncooked vegetables may be added to the above gravy and cooked till done. Add milk (½ cup) and pepper powder. Add one teaspoon fresh cream.

(vii) North Indian Gravy without Onion and Garlic

Ingredients	Quantity
Any vegetable (especially peas, potato, Brinjal and bottle gourd (1″ cubes) and Sprouted Bengal gram	½ kg

Ingredients	Quantity
Water	1 cup
Oil	1 tsp
Cumin	¼ tsp
Green chilli	2
Ginger (paste or pieces)	½ tsp
Red chilli powder	1 tsp
Turmeric powder	a pinch
Salt	to taste
Amchur powder (raw mango powder)	1 tsp
or	
Thick tamarind extract (optional)	
Cumin–coriander seed powder	1 tsp
Tomato (cut into quarters/liquidised)	2–3
or	
Curd	2 tbsp
Any flour	1–2 tsp
Whole groundnuts (with husk)	12
or	
Cashewnuts	12
or	
Khus khus (optional)	2 tsp
or	
Sesame seeds	2 tsp

(Whole groundnuts / Cashewnuts / Khus khus / Sesame seeds: ground into a paste)

Method

1. Cook the vegetable in water.
2. To hot oil, add cumin, green chilli, ginger, red chilli powder, turmeric powder, salt, amchur or tamarind paste, cumin-coriander seed powder and tomato (liquidised or chopped) and/or curd.
3. Fry for 1–2 minutes, add water and boil till the gravy is formed.
4. Add the cooked vegetable.
5. To thicken the gravy, crush a few pieces of the pre- cooked vegetable pieces or add a slurry of any flour in a little water. The paste of groundnut/cashewnut/sesame/khus khus may also be added.

Note: The addition of poppy seeds or fresh coconut (grated) (2 teaspoons each) while grinding the masala, or adding a paste of these two after the masala is roasted, adds flavour and richness to the gravy.

(viii) North Indian Gravy with Onion and Garlic

Method A:

Ingredients	Quantity
Any pre-cooked vegetable (1 cm cubes)	½ kg
Oil	1 tsp
Onion } finely chopped	1 cup
Ginger } or grated	1 tsp
Garlic	1 tsp
Turmeric powder	a pinch
Salt	to taste
Tomato (finely cut)	¼ or ½ cup
Garam masala powder (optional) or	a pinch
Coriander seed powder or	½ tsp
Cumin powder	½ tsp
Water	1 cup

Method

1. Heat oil in a *kadai*. Add onion, ginger and garlic. Keep *kadai* on low fire stirring intermittently until it thickens and is cooked.
2. Add turmeric powder, salt, and tomato. Mix and cover the *kadai* with a lid till tomato softens.
3. Add garam masala powder, coriander seed powder or cumin powder.
4. Add water and boil. Add this gravy to any pre-cooked vegetable.

Method B:

Ingredients	Quantity
Any pre-cooked vegetable	½ kg.
Onion (finely chopped)	1 cup
Garlic	6–8 flakes
Ginger	½" piece
Tomato (1 cm cubes)	½ cup

Ingredients	Quantity
Turmeric powder	a pinch
Oil	1 tsp
Water	1 cup
Red chilli powder	1 tsp
Coriander–cumin seed powder	1 tsp
Garam masala powder (optional)	¼ tsp

Method

1. Grind onion, garlic, ginger, tomatoes and turmeric powder together.
2. Heat the ground paste in a hot *kadai* and keep on medium fire, till paste thickens.
3. Then add 1 tsp oil and fry for a minute or two. Add water and boil.
4. Add red chilli powder and coriander–cumin seed powder and garam masala powder.
5. Add any cooked vegetable.

Method C:

Use the same ingredients as Method B
1. Fry onion, ginger, garlic and tomato in oil and grind into a paste.
2. Add this along with a cup of water to the vegetable. This gravy has a distinctive flavour and taste.

Notes: (i) The addition of fresh cream (1 tsp) or a little milk (1 tablespoon/ ¼ cup) gives a creamy taste to the gravy and may be added to any of the three gravies given above.

(ii) Any vegetable, especially cauliflower, bottle gourd and chow-chow, may be used alone or combined with a few potatoes in all three methods.

(ix) Green Gravy

Ingredients	Quantity
Potato, peas, beans, carrot, cauliflower and Cabbage, chow-chow (finely cut) (and cooked in ½ cup water)	½ kg

Ingredients	Quantity
Oil	1 tsp
Onion (grated or finely chopped)	½ cup
Garlic	5–6 flakes
Ginger } grated/finely ground	½" piece
Green chilli	2
Coriander leaves (finely grind)	¼ cup
Cashewnut/groundnut with husk (finely grind)	1 dozen
Tomato (1 cm cubes) (ripe or half-ripe)	½ cup
Water	½ cup

Method

1. Fry onion in oil. When it becomes brownish, add paste of garlic, ginger and green chilli and fry a little.
2. Add the paste of coriander leaves, and then cashewnuts/ groundnuts paste. These should not be fried too much.
3. Add chopped tomato. Fry very lightly; see that the bits of tomato do not get mashed.
4. Add water, cooked vegetables, salt and mix well.

(x) Other gravies

(a)

Ingredients	Quantity
Brinjal, bottle gourd, tinda, beans (finely cut and cooked in 1 cup water)	½ kg
Black gram	1 tsp
Mustard	½ tsp
Curry leaves	6–8
Garlic (crushed)	1 or 2 flakes
Cumin powder	¼ tsp
Coriander seed powder	1 tsp
Fresh coconut (grated) } ground	1 tbsp
Ginger } into a paste	1" piece
Water (optional)	1 cup

Method

1. To a seasoning of black gram, mustard, and curry leaves, add garlic, cumin powder and coriander seed powder.

2. Add coconut and ginger paste.
3. Add cooked vegetables and boil for a minute.

(b)

Ingredients		Quantity
Bottle gourd/chow-chow/cabbage/brinjal and mixed vegetables (finely cut and cooked in 1 cup water)		½ kg
Oil		1 tsp
Onion (finely chopped)		1 cup
Coriander seed		1 tsp
Ginger		½" piece
Pepper	fried in 1 tsp oil and ground into a paste	2–3 cloves
Garlic		3–4 flakes
Green chilli		1
Red chilli		2
Fresh coconut (grated)		1 tbsp
Coriander leaves		A few sprigs
Seasoning		
Oil		1 tsp
Black gram		1 tsp
Mustard		½ tsp
Curry leaves		6–8

Method

1. To the paste add the cooked vegetables.
2. Boil for a while and season with mustard, black gram and curry leaves.

Note: Coriander seed and pepper may be omitted. Instead, roasted sesame seed (1 tsp) and uncooked ripe tomato (finely chopped, ¼ cup) may also be ground along with the other ingredients for the paste.

(c)

Ingredients	Quantity
Chow-chow/bottle gourd/ridge gourd/smooth Gourd (finely cut) (cooked in 1 cup water)	½ kg
Water (optional)	1 cup
Salt	to taste

Ingredients		Quantity
Fresh coconut (grated)		1 tbsp
Bengal gram (roasted)		1 tsp
Green chillies	grind to	1 or 2
Coriander leaves (finely chopped)	a paste	½ cup
Cumin		¼ tsp
Turmeric powder		a pinch
Seasoning		
Oil		1 tsp
Mustard		½ tsp
Red chilli		1 or 2
Curry leaves		6–8

Method

1. Heat oil in a *kadai*. Add mustard, red chilli and curry leaves.
2. Add cooked vegetables, salt and the paste.
3. Boil for a few minutes.

(d)

Ingredients	Quantity
Cauliflower, any other vegetable, mixed vegetables with potato (finely cut and cooked in 1 cup water)	½ kg
Water (optional)	1 cup
Tomato (1 cm cubes)	½ cup
Jaggery to taste	
Salt	to taste
Red chilli powder	
Seasoning	
Oil	1 tsp
Mustard	½ tsp
Asafoetida	a pinch
Onion (finely chopped)	½ cup
Ginger (paste or pieces)	½ tsp
Garlic (paste or pieces)	½ tsp

Method

1. Season mustard, asafoetida, onion, ginger and garlic in a *kadai*.
2. Add cooked vegetables, tomato and jaggery, salt and red chilli powder. Cook for a few minutes.

Note: Optional: Add raw mustard paste ($\frac{1}{2}$ teaspoon) or a paste of cinnamon ($\frac{1}{2}$" piece), cloves (1 or 2), peppercorns (1 or 2) and mix. Remove immediately from fire.

(e)

Ingredients	Quantity
Mixed vegetables (including 1 potato and 1 onion) (finely cut and cooked in 2 cups of water)	$\frac{1}{2}$ kg
Seasoning	
Oil	1 tsp
Black gram	1 tsp
Mustard	$\frac{1}{2}$ tsp
Green chilli (paste)	$\frac{1}{4}$ tsp
Asafoetida	a pinch
Curry leaves	6–8
Tomato (finely cut)	$\frac{1}{2}$ cup
Whole wheat flour	1 or 2 tsp

Method

1. Boil vegetables in water.
2. When cooked, season with black gram, mustard, green chilli paste, asafoetida, curry leaves, tomato and whole wheat flour.
3. Boil for 1 minute.

2. RECIPES FOR WET and/or DRY VEGETABLES

Wet or Dry Vegetables with Whole Pulses (Gram)

(i) With Roasted or Whole Pulses

Ingredients	Quantity
Any vegetable except potato, sweet potato, colocasia, lady's fingers, yam and corn	$\frac{1}{2}$ kg
Red gram	$\frac{1}{2}$ cup
Water	$\frac{1}{2}$ cup
Seasoning	
Ghee	$\frac{1}{2}$–1 tsp
Mustard	$\frac{1}{2}$ tsp
Cumin	$\frac{1}{2}$ tsp
Asafoetida	a pinch

Ingredients	Quantity
or	
Garlic (pieces or paste)	6–8 flakes
Curry leaves	6–8
Red chilli	1
Green chilli (pieces or paste)	1–2

Method

1. Dry roast red gram (½ cup) on low heat till it is slightly brown. (This adds a mild aroma).
2. Pressure cook the roasted red gram in water.
3. Cook vegetable in ½ cup water separately and then mix with red gram. Alternatively, half-cook the roasted red gram, add the vegetable and cook till done.
4. Season with mustard, cumin, asafoetida or garlic, curry leaves, red chilli and green chilli.
5. Add salt and mix well. Remove from fire.

Notes:

(a) Instead of roasted red gram, split pulses (preferably husked), other whole pulses like whole Bengal gram, whole green gram, whole lentil, whole matki or any whole pulses, soaked or sprouted may also be used.

(b) The pulses and vegetable can be cooked together if the cooking time for both is roughly the same as in the case of bottle gourd and green gram or presoaked pulses. Mix the soaked pulses and vegetable and pressure cook without adding any water. However, if the cooking time of the pulses is more than that of the vegetable, cook the pulses and then add the vegetable. Cook till the vegetable is done. You may also cook them separately.

(c) Dal should not be overcooked or mashed. The grains should remain separate.

(d) Fresh coconut (grated) (1–2 teaspoon) or a coarsely ground paste of fresh coconut, red chilli and cumin (¼ teaspoon) may also be added to enhance the taste.

(e) Finely chopped coriander leaves (¼ cup) may be added either alone or in combination with fresh, coconut (grated).

(f) Add finely chopped onion (¼ cup) in the seasoning. This is particularly suitable for raw jackfruit cooked by this method.

(g) Add coarsely-ground garlic to the seasoning. This is particularly suitable for pumpkin, kundru, radish, turnip and tinda.

(ii) With Dal Paste (Patholi)

Ingredients	Quantity
Cluster beans/French beans/any other beans (finely chopped)	½ kg
Red gram/Bengal gram (soaked)	½ cup
Water	1 cup
Green or red chilli	2
Asafoetida	a pinch
Salt	to taste
Turmeric powder	a pinch
Fresh coconut (grated) (for garnishing)	1 tsp

grind { Red gram/Bengal gram (soaked), Water, Green or red chilli, Asafoetida, Salt, Turmeric powder }

Seasoning

Oil	1 tsp
Black gram	½ tsp
Mustard	½ tsp
Cumin	¼ tsp
Red chilli	2
Curry leaves	6–8
Onion (finely chopped) (optional)	½ cup

Method

1. Wash red gram/Bengal gram and soak in water for about 2–3 hours.

2. Drain the water completely and grind gram to the consistency of fine semolina, along with green or red chilli, asafoetida, salt and turmeric powder.

3. Steam cook in idli plates or in any other pan for 5–7 minutes. Cool and break up the lump into a coarse powder.

4. Season, black gram, mustard, cumin, red chillies, curry leaves and onion (optional) in oil.

5. Add steamed vegetable and salt and mix well. Keep on a low flame, stirring intermittently till the water evaporates and the vegetable is dry. Garnish with fresh coconut (grated) (optional).

Notes:

  (a) Use the water in which the pulses have been soaked for other gravy vegetables. Do not throw it as it contains water- soluble vitamins and minerals.

  (b) Preferably use pulses with husk, since they have better nutritive value.

  (c) Use whole, sprouted pulses, as these have the best nutritive value.

Wet or Dry Vegetables without Pulses

(i) Frying uncooked vegetables in minimum oil and with/without potato

Ingredients	Quantity
Green peas/spinach and potato/any other vegetable with or without potato and/or onion (finely chopped or 1 cm cubes)	½ kg
Oil	2 tsp

Method

  1. Heat oil in a *kadai*. Add the pieces of vegetable, sprinkle a little water, and cover. Pour water on the lid and leave it undisturbed for 5–10 minutes to cook on a low fire. The water on the lid helps the vegetable to cook in its own water content. As the water in the vegetable vapourises, it meets the cold surface of the lid and gets condensed. The vegetable thus cooks in its own water.

  2. When half-done, add salt, mix, cover with a lid (with water on top) and leave on low fire till done. Sprinkle a few drops of water on the vegetable if and when necessary.

  3. For a fried taste, remove the lid and leave the vegetable on a low fire for a few minutes, stirring intermittently. Add 1–2 teaspoons of oil just before removing from fire.

Note: Since very little oil is used and some water is used, the vegetable may char/stick to the *kadai*. This is unavoidable and hence the need for the above-mentioned care and procedure.

(ii) Frying steamed vegetables with minimum oil with/without potato

Ingredients	Quantity
Bottle gourd/yam/colocasia/cluster beans with potato or a combination of English vegetables with potato (finely chopped or 1 cm cubes)	½ kg

Method

1. Steam cook in a pressure cooker or any other pan. If the steaming is done in a pan, take a cup of water in a pan or *kadai*. When it boils, place a stainless steel sieve over the mouth. Place the vegetables to be steamed in the sieve, cover it with a lid and keep on low heat till the vegetable gets cooked. If a pressure cooker is being used, pour a glass of water into the pressure cooker and place a stainless steel ring in it [like the one placed under an earthenware/brass/stainless steel pot (*ghada*)]. On the ring, place a stainless steel sieve with the vegetable to be steamed in it. (You may use a plate if there are fewer vegetables.) Close the lid of the cooker and cook till done. When cool, remove. Vegetable steamed this way is dry. In all cases and under all circumstances, the water in which vegetables are steamed or cooked must be used either as soup, or to make gravy or drunk as it is with or without salt and/or jaggery, as this water contains all the water-soluble nutrients of the vegetable. If either the ring or the sieve is not available, place a pan in the cooker and put the vegetable to be steamed in it and steam as above.

Fry these steamed vegetables as follows:

(a) *On a tava*: Frying on a *tava* is faster, more efficient, and requires less oil than frying in a *kadai*. On a hot *tava* (frying pan) smear ½ teaspoon oil and add the steamed vegetables. When they are brown, turn the pieces over and roast (fry) again on a medium fire adding ½ teaspoon oil. Sprinkle salt, red chilli powder and remove from fire. Repeat in batches if necessary.

(b) *In a kadai*: Heat 1 tbsp oil in a *kadai*. Add onion (optional), the steamed vegetable, and fry on low fire, turning the pieces intermittently. Add salt, red chilli powder and remove from fire.

Seasonings, Dressings and Spices, Herbs and Garnishings for Steamed Vegetables

These steamed vegetables, can have dressing, seasoning and spices, herbs and garnishings added to enhance taste, nutritive value and flavour. Some suggestions are given below. These can be tried on a variety of vegetables, besides the ones suggested here. The amount of each ingredient can be varied to taste.

Method of preparation

Steam/boil ½ kg vegetable in ½ cup water. Add any one of the seasonings and additives given below. Keep on fire for a minute or two and remove.

(i) Simple Seasoning of Steamed Vegetables—South Indian

Ingredients	Quantity
Almost any vegetable like cabbage/cauliflower, carrot, beans, chow-chow, brinjal, bottle gourd, ridge gourd, smooth gourd, snake gourd, beetroot, kundru (small pieces)	½ kg
Salt	to taste
Seasoning	
Oil	½ tsp
Black gram	½ tsp
Mustard	¼ tsp
Cumin	¼ tsp
Asafoetida	a pinch
Green chilli (paste or pieces)	½ tsp
Red chilli	2 or 3
or	
Red chilli powder	¼ tsp
Curry leaves	6–8

Method

1. Steam or cook the vegetable in minimum water.
2. Add salt and season with black gram, mustard, cumin, asafoetida, green chilli, red chilli (or red chilli powder) and curry leaves.

(ii) Simple Seasoning of Steamed Vegetables with Ginger

Ingredients	Quantity
All varieties of gourd/brinjal/raw banana/kundru (small pieces)	½ kg
Ginger or garlic (pieces or paste)	to taste

Method

1. Add pieces of ginger or ginger paste and green chilli to the seasoning for **Recipe (i)**.
2. Alternatively, use a few crushed garlic flakes or garlic paste because these go well with vegetables like gourds, chow-chow and kundru.

(iii) Simple Seasoning of Steamed Vegetables with Fresh Grated Coconut

Ingredients	Quantity
Any vegetable like cabbage, cauliflower, beans (all varieties), carrot, green peas, beetroot (small pieces)	½ kg
Fresh coconut (grated)	2 tbsp
Turmeric powder	a pinch

Method

1. To the seasoning in **Recipe (i)** add boiled/steamed/fried vegetable, salt, fresh grated coconut and turmeric powder.
2. Fry for a minute and remove from fire.
   (Instead of adding just grated coconut, add a coarsely-ground paste of coconut and green chilli.)

(iv) *Simple Seasoning of Steamed Vegetables with Onion, Coriander Leaves and Coconut (optional)*

Ingredients	Quantity
Any vegetable like cabbage, cauliflower, carrot, beetroot, flat beans, cluster beans and other varieties of beans, gourds (small pieces)	½ kg
Onion (finely chopped)	¼ cup
Coriander leaves (finely chopped)	¼ cup
Fresh coconut (grated)	1 tbsp

Method

1. To the seasoning in recipe (i) add onion and fry.
2. Garnish with coriander leaves and grated coconut and mix well. If green leafy vegetables are used, avoid garnishing with coriander leaves.

(v) *Simple Seasoning of Steamed Vegetables with Various Powders (see chapter 18 for their preparation)*

Ingredients	Quantity
Any vegetable like carrot, cabbage, beans, cauliflower, beetroot, bottle gourd, snake gourd, smooth gourd, ridge gourd, brinjal, chow-chow, potato, kundru (small pieces)	½ kg
Rasam/sambar/curry or other powder	1–1½ tsp

Method

1. Season the dry vegetable as in recipe (i) and add any of the following powders: rasam/sambar, curry leaves, roasted poppy seed, groundnut, bisibela, Iyengar pulihodarai (pulihara), and roasted sesame seed.

a) With Dal Powder or Curry Powder

Ingredients	Quantity
Brinjal/cabbage/cauliflower/tinda/carrot/gourds/chow-chow/beans (all varieties) (small or 1" long pieces)	½ kg
Onion (1" long pieces)	¼ cup
Fresh coconut (grated) (optional)	1 tbsp

Ingredients	Quantity
Oil	1 tsp
For the Curry Powder	
Oil	½ tsp
Bengal gram	1 tbsp
Black gram	½ tbsp
Coriander seed (optional) ⎱ roasted	¼ tsp
Cumin	¼ tsp
Red chilli	2
Asafoetida	a pinch

Method

1. Dry roast or fry all the ingredients for the curry powder in a *kadai*. Pound them into a not-too-coarse powder and keep aside.
2. To hot oil, add onion and fry till cooked.
3. Add steamed vegetable (without any water), salt, curry powder and coconut. Mix well and remove from fire.

b) With Curry (Dal) Powder, Raw Onion and Coconut

Ingredients	Quantity
French beans/kundru/brinjal/bottle gourd (small or 1" long pieces)	½ kg
Curry powder	2–3 tsp
Onion (finely chopped)	1 cup
Fresh coconut (grated)	1 tbsp
Green chilli	2

Method

1. To the curry powder in **Recipe v(a)** add onion, coconut and green chilli and pound or grind coarsely in a food processor.
2. Add this to the steamed vegetable (steamed without water).

(vi) Steamed Sour Vegetables with Ginger Paste (Pulusu Pettina Kura)

Ingredients	Quantity
Brinjal/raw banana/banana stem (pith)/raw jackfruit/ bottle gourd/tinda/raw papaya/cabbage (small pieces)	½ kg
Turmeric powder	a pinch
Thick tamarind extract	2 tsp

Ingredients	Quantity
Seasoning	
Oil	1 tsp
Bengal gram	1 tsp
Black gram	1 tsp
Mustard	$1/2$ tsp
Green chilli	1
Red chilli	1
Curry leaves	6–8
Ginger	$1/2$" piece
Cumin	$1/2$ tsp
Green chilli	1

ground to a paste

Method

1. To the steamed vegetables add turmeric powder and thick tamarind extract.
2. Season with the ingredients given above.
3. Cook for a minute and lightly mash the vegetable.

(vii) Steamed Sour Vegetables with Mustard Paste (Aava Pettina Kura)

Ingredients	Quantity
Raw jackfruit/raw banana/cabbage/ banana stem (pith) (small pieces)	$1/2$ kg
Mustard	1 tsp
Fresh coconut (grated)	1 or 2 tbsp
Green chilli	1
Jaggery	a small lump

Method

Prepare the vegetable as in (vi) above. Just before removing from fire, add finely ground raw mustard paste or a paste of mustard, coconut, green chilli and jaggery.

(viii) Steamed Sweet and Sour Vegetables

Ingredients	Quantity
Kundru/bottle gourd/cluster beans/pumpkin (small pieces)	$1/2$ kg

Ingredients	Quantity
Jaggery	1 or 2 lime-size pieces
Rice or whole wheat flour	2 tsp

Method

1. Cook as in **Recipe (vi)**. However, instead of ginger and cumin paste add jaggery for sweetness.
2. Add rice flour or whole wheat flour a minute or two before removing from fire. This will make the gravy thicker.

(ix) Upma Seasoning of Steamed Vegetables

Ingredients	Quantity
Potato/raw banana/raw jackfruit/ capsicum with potato (small pieces)	½ kg
Oil	1 tsp
Bengal gram	1 tsp
Black gram	1 tsp
Mustard	½ tsp
Curry leaves	6–8
Green chilli (paste/pieces)	½ tsp
Ginger (paste/pieces)	½–1 tsp
Onion (finely chopped)	1 cup
Salt	to taste
Turmeric (optional)	a pinch

Method

1. To the seasoning add the steamed vegetable, salt and turmeric powder (optional).
2. Mix well and mash lightly, keep on low heat for a minute or two and remove. Sprinkle a little water if needed.

(x) A Few More Pastes for Steamed Vegetables

a) Raw Onion and Coconut Paste

Ingredients	Quantity
French beans/brinjal/kundru/tinda (small pieces)	½ kg

Ingredients	Quantity
For the paste	
Onion (1 cm cubes)	¾ cup
Fresh coconut (grated)	2 tbsp
Green chilli (paste/pieces)	2
Cumin	1 tsp
Salt	to taste

Method

Coarsely pound the ingredients for the paste together and add to vegetable.

b) Raw Onion with Tamarind/Raw Mango/Indian Gooseberry Paste

Ingredients	Quantity
Brinjal/carrot/colocasia/potato (1" long pieces)	½ kg
For the paste	
Tamarind/mango/green tamarind/	½ lime-sized
Indian gooseberry	or 1 tbsp bits
Onion (finely chopped)	¾ cup
Red/green chilli	2
Cumin	1 tsp
Salt	to taste

Method

Coarsely grind the ingredients for the paste together and add to the vegetables.

Colocasia and Potato Curry

Ingredients	Quantity
Colocasia/potato (1" long pieces)	½ kg
Seasoning	
Oil	3 tsp
Black gram	1 tsp
Mustard	½ tsp
Curry leaves	6–8
Red chillies	to taste
Onion (1" long pieces)	1 cup or more

Method

1. To the seasoning add pre-boiled colocasia, and the ground paste and mix.
2. Fry on low fire, stirring frequently till fried to redness.

c) Coriander Leaves with Coconut Paste

Ingredients	Quantity
Brinjal/carrot/beans/tinda (1" long pieces)	½ kg
For the paste	
Coriander leaves (finely chopped)	2 cups
Fresh coconut (grated)	¼–½ cup
Green chilli	2
cumin	¼ cup
salt	to taste

Method

Grind into a medium-coarse paste and add to vegetable.

d) Coriander Leaves with Ginger Paste

Ingredients	Quantity
Beans/brinjal/carrot/cauliflower (small pieces)	½ kg
For the paste	
Coriander leaves (finely chopped)	2 cups
Green chillies	2
Ginger	½" piece
Fresh coconut (grated)	½ cup
Poppy seed (raw or roasted) (optional)	1 tbsp
Salt	to taste

Method

Grind all the ingredients well and add to vegetable.

e) Coriander Leaves with Coriander Seed Paste

Ingredients	Quantity
Chou-chou/gourds/raw banana (small pieces)	½ kg

Ingredients	Quantity
Oil	½ tsp
Coriander leaves (finely chopped)	¾–1 cup
Green chilli	1
For the paste	
Water	2 tbsp
Coriandar seeds	1 tsp
Garlic	6 flakes
Ginger	1" piece
Fresh coconut (grated)	1 tbsp
Cumin	¼ tsp
Onion (finely cut)	½ cup

Method

1. Roast coriander leaves and green chilli in oil.
2. Grind these along with the other ingredients into a paste.

f) Poppy Seed Paste

Ingredients	Quantity
Chow-chow/cabbage/gourds (small pieces)	½ kg
For the paste	
Poppy seed	2 tbsp
Salt	to taste
Cumin	a pinch
Sugar	1 pinch
Green chilli	2
Turmeric powder	a pinch

Method

Grind the ingredients together and add to steamed vegetable, sprinkling a little water.

g) Poppy Seed with Pepper Paste

Ingredients	Quantity
Chow-chow/beans (small pieces)	½ kg
For the paste	
Poppy seed	2 tbsp

Ingredients	Quantity
Pepper corns	1/2 tsp
Cardamoms	2
Green chilli	1
Salt	to taste
Additional ingredients:	
Onion (finely chopped)	1/2 cup
Ginger	1/2" piece
Coriander seed	1 tsp
Garlic	6 flakes

Method

1. Grind the ingredients into a paste.
2. The additional ingredients may be added, if necessary, while grinding the paste.

h) Coriander Seed with Coconut Paste

Ingredients	Quantity
Any vegetable except the leafy ones (small pieces)	1/2 kg
For the paste	
Cumin	1/4 tsp
Coriander seeds	1 tsp
Red chilli	1
Salt	to taste
Turmeric powder	a pinch
Fresh coconut (grated)	2 tbsp
Water	1/4 cup

Method

Grind all the ingredients into a paste and add to vegetable.

(xi) Steamed Vegetables with Panch Phoran Masala (Bengali Style)

Ingredients	Quantity
Ash gourd, pumpkin, sweet potato, spinach, cabbage, brinjal, capsicum, radish, smooth gourd (cut into 1" square chunks)	1/2 kg

Ingredients		Quantity
Turmeric powder		a pinch
Sugar or jaggery		1 tsp
Salt		to taste
For the powder/paste		
Coriander seed	⎫	1 tsp
Cumin	⎬ (finely ground)	¼ tsp
Bay leaf	⎭	1
or		
Ginger	⎫ (finely ground)	½" piece
Garlic	⎭	3 or 4 flakes
Seasoning		
Oil		1 tbsp
Mustard		¼ tsp
Onion seed		¼ tsp
Fenugreek seed		¼ tsp or less
Cumin		¼ tsp
Aniseed		¼ tsp
Red or green chilli		1
Bay leaves		2
Garnishing		
Curry leaves		a few

Method

1. Combine all the ingredients of the seasoning, add vegetables, turmeric powder and sugar or jaggery and cook for a minute or two. Remove from fire.
2. Add either the powder or the paste and garnish with curry leaves.

Note: For all these recipes use cooked vegetables. If, however, uncooked vegetables are to be used, first cook the pieces of potato on low fire in 1 tbsp oil, covering the pan with a lid on which water is poured. When half-done, add pieces of radish, gourd, beans, ash gourd, red pumpkin, sweet potato, carrot, cauliflower, spinach, cabbage, brinjal, capsicum and cook till done.

(xii) Steamed Vegetables with Onion Seed

Ingredients	Quantity
Cauliflower and potatoes (½" pieces)	½ kg
Ginger	½" piece
Garlic	6–8 flakes
Turmeric powder	a pinch
Garam masala powder	½ tsp
or	
Cloves	4–6
Cinnamon } Powdered together	¼" piece
cardamom	1

Seasoning

Oil	1 tbsp
Onion seeds	½ tsp
Bay leaves	2

Method

1. Season onion seed and bay leaves in a little oil. Add pieces of potato.
2. Cook, covering pan with a lid on which water has been poured. Leave undisturbed for 5 minutes on low fire. Mix, sprinkle a little water and cover again.
3. When cooked add the steamed vegetable. Add turmeric powder, a little water, salt, ginger–garlic paste and cook on low fire for a minute.
4. Add garam masala or cloves–cinnamon–cardamom powder and remove from fire immediately.

(xiii) Steamed Vegetables (Maharashtrian Style)

Ingredients	Quantity
Vegetables like cluster beans, pumpkin (small bits)	½ kg
Jaggery (powder)	½ tsp
Maharashtrian (kala) masala powder	1 tsp
Turmeric powder	1 pinch
Salt	to taste
Water	¼ cup

Ingredients	Quantity
Seasoning	
Oil	1 tsp
Mustard	½ tsp
Asafoetida	a pinch
Curry leaves	6–8
Green chilli	1
Onion (finely chopped) (optional)	¼ cup
Garnishing	
Coriander leaves (finely chopped)	¼ cup
Fresh coconut (grated)	1 tbsp

Method

1. To the seasoning add steamed vegetable, water, salt, jaggery, Maharashtrian kala masala (page 279) powder and turmeric powder and mix well.
2. Garnish with coriander leaves and grated coconut.

Note: If leafy vegetables are used, then omit, mustard, turmeric powder and coriander leaves. Season with pounded ginger and/or garlic instead.

(xiv) Steamed Vegetables with Dry Ginger Powder/ Fresh Ginger

Ingredients	Quantity
Knol-khol/ridge gourd/bottle Gourd/kundru (small pieces)	½ kg
Water	1 cup
Salt	to taste
Seasoning	
Oil	1 tbsp
Dry ginger powder	1 tsp
Aniseed powder	2 tsp
Coriander seed powder	1 tsp
Red chilli powder	½ tsp
Garam masala powder	¼ tsp

Method

1. To the seasoning add steamed vegetable with water and salt.

2. Mix well and remove from fire.

(xv) Steamed Vegetables with Onion and Tomato

Ingredients	Quantity
Cabbage/cauliflower/carrot/beans/brinjal/ smooth gourd and ridge gourd (small pieces)	½ kg
Oil	1 tsp
Cumin	¼ tsp
Asafoetida	a pinch
Onion (finely chopped or sliced)	½ cup
Tomato (1" pieces)	1 cup
Water	½ cup
Red chilli powder	½ tsp
Salt	to taste

Method

1. Roast cumin, asafoetida and onion in oil.
2. When fried add tomato and cook for a few minutes till tomato softens.
3. Add the steamed vegetables, water, red chilli powder and salt. Keep on low fire for a minute and remove.

(xvi) Steamed Vegetables with Onion, Tomato and Ginger

Ingredients	Quantity
Cabbage/beans/brinjals/gourds (small pieces)	½ kg
Oil	1 tsp
Onion (finely chopped)	1 cup
Green chilli (paste)	½ tsp
Ginger (paste)	½" piece
Tomato (1 cm cubes)	1 cup
Turmeric powder	a pinch
Water	½ cup

Method

1. Fry onion, green chilli, ginger and tomato in oil.
2. Add turmeric powder and cook for a few minutes.
3. Add steamed vegetable, and water and cook on low fire for a minute.

(xvii) Steamed Vegetables (with Groundnut Powder) (Maharashtrian Style)

Ingredients	Quantity
Vegetables like raw papaya, cluster Beans, pumpkin (finely chopped)	½ kg
Water	½ cup
Salt	to taste
Turmeric powder	a pinch
Maharashtrian kala masala powder	2 tsp
Roasted groundnut unhusked (powder)	2 tsp
Fresh coconut (grated)	2 tsp
Coriander leaves (finely chopped)	1 tsp
Thick tamarind extract (optional)	2 tsp
Jaggery (powder)	½ tsp

Seasoning

Oil	½ tsp
Mustard	½ tsp
Asafoetida	a pinch
Curry leaves	6
Green chilli	2
Onion (finely chopped)	½ cup

Method

1. To the seasoning add steamed vegetable, salt, turmeric powder, Maharashtrian kala masala powder, groundnut powder, coconut, coriander, thick tamarind extract and jaggery.
2. Keep on fire for a minute and remove.

(xviii) Steamed Vegetables with/without Onion and Garlic— North Indian Style (wet preparation) - see pages 64 and 62

Ingredients	Quantity
Suitable vegetables: almost all vegetables like cabbage, beans, brinjal, gourds (small pieces)	½ kg

Note: Instead of being made into a paste, all the ingredients can be finely chopped. In addition to the above ingredients, coriander leaves (½ cup finely chopped) can also be added while seasoning.

(xix) Sweet and Sour Steamed Vegetables

Ingredients	Quantity
Bottle gourd/cluster beans/kundru/cabbage (1 cm cubes)	½ kg
Water	½ cup
Salt	to taste
Thick tamarind extract	2 tbsp
Jaggery	2 lime-sized balls
Turmeric powder	a pinch
Any flour (whole wheat, rice or Bengal gram)	1–2 tsp
Seasoning	
Oil	1 tsp
Black gram	1 tsp
Cumin	½ tsp
Asafoetida	a pinch
Red chilli	2
Curry leaves	6–8

Method

1. Steam vegetable with water, and add salt, tamarind extract, jaggery and turmeric powder.
2. Add the seasoning.
3. Add flour to thicken, mix well, leave on fire for a minute or two. Remove from fire.

(xx) Gujarati Pav Bhaji with Steamed Vegetables

Ingredients	Quantity
Cauliflower (small florets)	½ cup
Carrot (small pieces)	½ cup
Green peas (shelled)	½ cup
Beans (finely cut)	½ cup
Cabbage (finely chopped)	½ cup
Potatoes (boiled and mashed)	1 cup
Oil	2 tsp
Onion (finely chopped)	½ cup

Ingredients	Quantity
Oil	1 tsp
Ginger (finely chopped)	little
Green chilli (finely chopped)	3 to 4
Garlic (finely chopped)	25 to 30 flakes
Tomato (finely cut)	1½ cups
Salt	to taste
Cumin powder	1 tsp
Garam masala powder	1 pinch
Red chilli powder	to taste
Butter or fresh cream	1–2 tsp
Lime juice (optional)	1–2 tsp
Whole wheat flour bread	6 slices

Garnishing

Coriander leaves (finely chopped)	2 tbsp
Onion (finely chopped)	2 tbsp

Method

1. Cook all the vegetables [cauliflower, carrot, peas, beans and cabbage] in a little water and mash.
2. Fry onion, ginger, green chilli, and garlic in oil till they turn light brown.
3. Add tomato and salt and cook.
4. Add all the above mashed vegetables and potatomash.
5. Add cumin powder, garam masala powder, red chilli powder to taste (and a little water if needed) and cook till it becomes a paste and is well blended (mixed).
6. Add butter (or fresh cream) and lime juice (optional).
7. Garnish with coriander leaves and onion (optional). Serve with toasted bread.

(xxi) Korma with Steamed Vegetables

a) Korma with Fried Ingredients

Ingredients	Quantity
Potato/mixed English vegetables (finely diced)	½ kg
Oil	1 tsp
Fresh coconut (grated)	½ cup

Ingredients	Quantity
Poppy seed	1 tbsp
Cinnamon	1" piece
Green chilli	1–2
Onion (finely chopped)	1 cup
Garlic	3–4 flakes
Ginger	½" piece
Seasoning	
Oil	1 tsp
Clove	2
Cinnamon	½" piece
cashewnut	3–4
Bay leaves	1–2
Bread crumbs (optional)	2 tbsp

Method

1. Roast coconut, poppy seed, cinnamon, cloves, green chilli, onion, garlic and ginger in oil and grind into a very fine paste.
2. Cook the potatoes mixed vegetables and mash them coarsely.
3. Add 2 cups of water, salt and the ground paste and boil well.
4. Season with cloves, pieces of cinnamon, cashewnuts and bay leaves and garnish with bread crumbs (optional).

b) Korma with raw ingredients

Ingredients	Quantity
Potato and English vegetables (finely diced)	½ kg
Cinnamon	½" piece
Cloves	2
Cardamom (small)	1
Poppy seed	2 tsp
Fresh coconut (grated)	2 tbsp
Coriander seed	2 tsp
Green chilli	1
Ginger	½" piece
Garlic	2–4 flakes
curd	½ cup
Oil	1 tsp
Onion (finely chopped)	1 cup

Ingredients	Quantity
Bay leaves	2
Water	2 cup

Method

1. Grind cinnamon, cloves, cardamom, poppy seed, coconut, coriander seed, green chilli, ginger, and garlic into a fine paste. Mix this paste with curd.
2. Fry onion in oil.
3. Add bay leaves, steamed (with 2 cups of water) vegetables and masala paste and mix well.
4. Remove from fire immediately. Do not boil gravies made with curd since they tend to 'split' if heated for too long.

3. RECIPES FOR STUFFED VEGETABLES

The vegetables generally used for stuffing are brinjal, kundru, smooth gourd, ridge gourd, snake gourd, bitter gourd, tinda, capsicum and lady's fingers.

Slit the vegetable into 2 or 4 keeping the base intact. Alternatively, slit from both ends of the vegetable in perpendicular directions so that it remains intact and does not break into 2 or 4 pieces.

General method of preparation (except for lady's fingers): Steam the stuffed vegetable in water ($^1/_2$ cup) in a *kadai* on low fire, or in a pressure pan or cooker. As soon as the pressure builds up and just before the first whistle, switch off the flame to avoid overcooking and making the vegetable soggy. Let the pan or cooker cool till the lid can be opened. Either let the water in the pan or cooker evaporate by keeping it on the fire without its lid or transfer the cooked vegetable along with the water on to a hot greased *tava* and roast. Turn over and roast again with $^1/_2$ teaspoon oil.

or

Let the water in the pan evaporate without removing the vegetable. Add $^1/_2$ tsp oil and keep for a few minutes. The stuffed vegetable will be slightly moist. When making stuffed lady's fingers do not steam. Instead, fry in 2–3 tsp oil in a *kadai*, cover with a lid and leave undisturbed for 5–10 minutes on low heat. Stir occasionally.

(i) Stuffing made with Coriander leaves (kothimiri kharam)

Ingredients	Quantity
Brinjal/snake gourd/parwal/tinda	½ kg
Dry roast and grind	
Coriander leaves (finely chopped)	1½ cups
Fresh coconut (grated)	2 tbsp
Green chlli	2
Cumin	½ tsp
Salt	to taste

Method

Grind the above ingredients coarsely and use for stuffing the vegetable.

(ii) Raw Onion, Red Chilli with Tamarind Stuffing (Ullikharam)

Ingredients	Quantity
Brinjal/tinda/kundru/ridge gourd/snake gourd	½ kg
Raw tamarind/raw mango (grated)	1 lime-sized ball
Onion (finely chopped)	1 cup
Red or green chilli	2
Cumin	½ tsp
Salt	to taste

Method

Coarsely grind raw tamarind/raw mango, onion, red or green chilli, cumin and salt. Use this for stuffing the vegetable.

(iii) Raw Onion-Red Chilli Stuffing

Ingredients	Quantity
Brinjal/ridge gourd/kundru/snake gourd	½ kg
Onion (finely chopped)	1 cup
Red or green chilli or red chilli powder	1 tsp
Cumin	½ tsp
Salt	to taste

Method

Grate or pound onion, red or green chilli/red chilli powder, cumin and salt. Use this for stuffing the vegetable.

(iv) Curry (Dal) Powder Stuffing

Ingredients	Quantity
Brinjal/ridge gourd/kundru/snake gourd/tinda/parwal/bitter gourd	½ kg
Oil	1 tsp
Bengal gram	2 tbsp
Black gram	1 tbsp
Coriander seed (optional)	1 tbsp
Mustard (optional)	1 tsp
Red chilli	2
Asafoetida	a pinch
Salt	to taste

Method

1. Roast and coarsely powder Bengal gram, black gram, coriander seed, mustard, red chilli, asafoetida.
2. Add salt. Use this for stuffing the vegetable.

Variations:

a) Pound the above curry powder with salt, raw onion (1 cup, 1 cm cut pieces), fresh coconut grating (2 tablespoons) and green chilli.

b) A little tamarind can also be added to impart a slight sourness.

(v) North Indian Stuffing

(a) Stuffing with Potato or Potato mixed with other Vegetables

Ingredients	Quantity
Capsicum/lady's fingers/snake gourd/tomato	½ kg
Potatoes with skin	¼ kg
Salt	to taste
Red chilli powder	1 tsp

Ingredients	Quantity
Fried/raw onion (finely chopped)	1 cup
Coriander seed powder	½ tsp
Cumin powder	1 tsp
Asafoetida	a pinch
Garam masala powder (optional)	a pinch

Method

1. Boil potatoes with skins intact in water or steam them.
2. Mash coarsely, add salt and the rest of the ingredients.

Alternatively, roast the following and use as stuffing.

Ingredients	Quantity
Coriander seed	1 tbsp
Cumin	1 tsp
Red chilli	1 or 2
Aniseed	1 tsp
Mustard	½ tsp
Tamarind (optional)	1 lime-sized ball
Salt	to taste
Garam masala powder	a pinch

Method

1. Fry coriander seed, cumin, red chilli and aniseed.
2. Grind with mustard, tamarind, salt and garam masala.
3. Add mashed potato and onion (fried in ½ teaspoon oil).

Note: Add brown bread crumbs or its powder to avoid sogginess (if any) of the meshed potato or fry the potato stuffing in 1 tsp oil on a *tava* for a few minutes on low fire. Cool and use.

Seal the slits of the stuffed vegetable with gram flour paste so that the masala does not leak out.

Finely cut or coarsely-grated vegetables like carrot,cabbage or baked brinjal can be added to the potato stuffing.

When stuffing vegetables like capsicum and tomato, scoop out their contents, mix them with the potato stuffing and use.

Stuffed lady's fingers should not be steamed. Cook the stuffed lady's fingers in 2–3 tsp hot oil in a *kadai*, cover with a lid on which water is poured, and leave undisturbed for 5–10 minutes on low flame. Stir occasionally till done. The same method can be followed for capsicum. First smearing the stuffed capsicums with a little oil will help in consuming less oil and making cooking faster.

(b) Stuffing without Potato

Ingredients	Quantity
Lady's fingers/brinjal/ridge gourd/ tinda/kundru/snake gourd	½ kg
Salt	to taste
Turmeric powder	a pinch
Red chilli powder	1 tsp
Cumin	1 tsp
Cumin powder	1 tsp
Coriander seed	1 tsp
Garam masala powder (optional)	a pinch
Bengal gram flour (optional)	1 tsp
Sugar (optional)	¼ tsp
Oil (optional)	½ tsp

Method

Mix all the ingredients together and use as stuffing.

(vi) Thyme–Gram Flour Stuffing

Ingredients	Quantity
Brinjal/capsicum/lady's fingers	½ kg
Bengal gram flour	1 tbsp
thyme	½ tsp
Coriander seed powder	1 tsp
Cumin powder	1 tsp
Sesame seed	1 tsp
Fresh coconut (grated)	1 tbsp
Salt	to taste
Turmeric powder	a pinch
Red chilli powder	1 tsp
Jaggery	to taste
Sesame seeds	1 tsp

Method

1. Mix all the ingredients together and use as stuffing.
2. Season with sesame seed in a little oil.

(vii) Onion–Aniseed Stuffing

Ingredients		Quantity
Brinjal		½ kg
Oil		1 tbsp
Onion (finely chopped)		1 cup
Green chilli		4
Ginger		¼" piece
Cumin	ground	1 tbsp
Salt	into a paste	to taste
Aniseed		1 tbsp
Green coriander (finely chopped)		½ cup
Fried onion (finely chopped)		½ cup
Raisins		12
Groundnuts		12
Salt		to taste
Turmeric powder		a pinch
Jaggery (powder)		½ tsp

Method

1. Grind raw and fried onion, green chilli, ginger, cumin, salt, aniseed, and green coriander. Stuff the brinjal with half of this paste.
2. Heat oil in a *kadai*. Add stuffed brinjal, stir and keep on low fire. Cover with a lid (on which water is poured). Leave undisturbed for about 10 minutes.
3. When half-done, add ½ cup water, the rest of the paste, raisins, groundnuts, salt, turmeric powder, jaggery and cook till done, without covering the *kadai*.

(viii) Poppy Seed Stuffing

Ingredients	Quantity
Brinjal	½ kg

Ingredients	Quantity
Poppy seed	1 tbsp
Fresh coconut (grated)	1 tbsp
Pepper corns	3–4
Cloves	3–4
Onion (finely chopped)	½ cup
Green chilli	2
Garlic	3–4 flakes

Method

Grind the ingredients into a fine paste. Use as stuffing for the vegetable.

(ix) Maharashtrian Masala Stuffing

Ingredients	Quantity
Brinjal, kundru	½ kg
Maharashtrian kala masala powder	1 tbsp
Roasted groundnuts (with skin) (powder)	1 tbsp
Salt	to taste
Roasted sesame seeds (powder)	1 tbsp
Jaggery	to taste
Red chilli powder	1 tbsp
Coriander leaves (finely chopped)	½ cup
Fresh coconut (grated)	1 tbsp
Tamarind (extract)	1 lime-sized ball
Seasoning	
Oil	1 tbsp
Mustard	½ tsp
Asafoetida	a pinch
Turmeric powder	a pinch
Onion (finely chopped)	½ cup
Water	1 cup

Method

1. Mix Maharashtrian kala masala powder, groundnut powder, salt, sesame seed powder, jaggery, red chilli powder, coriander leaves and coconut.
2. Stuff brinjal with the above mixture.

3. Heat oil and add seasoning. Fry a little, add stuffed brinjal, and tamarind extract and cook till done, adding water and the leftover masala paste, and cook till done.

Note: a) Maharashtrian masala powder may be substituted wth any other masala powder. b) Sesame seed powder and green coriander may be omitted.

8

Recipes for Single Vegetables with Spices, Herbs and Garnishings

In each recipe, $\frac{1}{2}$ kg of vegetable has been used. It makes six servings, unless indicated otherwise.

All the vegetables mentioned in this Chapter (except for some starchy ones and nuts) contain, per 100 g of edible portion,

High amounts of	*Low amounts of*
Water - 70–96 g	fat - 0.1–1.5 g
fibre - 0.6–5 g	energy - 10–100 kcal
minerals - 0.3–3 g	carbohydrates - 2–14 g
vitamins - one or all of the	proteins - 0.2–7 g
vitamins A, B and C	

Yellow, orange/red and green vegetables are especially rich in vitamin A (beta-carotene and carotenoids).

As a rule, all green leafy vegetables are rich in vitamins A, B and C in varying proportions and combinations. However just to indicate the amounts of vitamins in the vegetables and additives mentioned in this Chapter, an approximate quantity is given and is indicated by the terms low, moderate and high. — Indicates insignificant/nil quantity.

I. Ash Gourd (Ash Pumpkin, Wax Gourd)

Vitamins
Vitamin A: —
Vitamin B group: low
Vitamin C: low

This vegetable is alkaline and is very good for inflammations and ulcers anywhere in the body. It is a diuretic. It is good for diabetics.

(i) Ash Gourd with Pulses (3 servings)

Ingredients	Quantity
Ash gourd (1 cm cubes)	2 cups
Green gram with skin (pre-soaked)	½ cup
Water	½ cup
Salt	to taste
Seasoning	
Oil	½ tsp
Onion seed	½ tsp
Green chilli ⎫ ground into	½ tsp
Ginger ⎭ a paste	
Turmeric powder	a pinch

Method

1. Cook the vegetable with green gram and water.
2. Add salt after it is cooked.
3. Add seasoning and mash a little. [Approx. **36 cal/serving**]

(ii) Ash Pumpkin Vadas (8 servings)

Ingredients	Quantity
Ash gourd (coarsely grated or cut into thin 1" long strips)	4 cups or more
Split black gram without skin	1 cup
Water	2 cups
Green chilli	2
Asafoetida	a pinch
Salt	to taste
Oil	½ tsp

Method

1. Wash and soak black gram in water for 3–4 hours.
2. Drain water and grind into a fine thick paste with green chilli, asafoetida and salt.
3. Add ash gourd and mix well adding a little water if necessary.
4. On a hot greased *tava*, spread the batter to 3" diameter and fry on one side.
5. Then turn over and fry the other side with ½ tsp oil. Serve hot. [Approx. **61 cal/serving**]

Note: When the vegetable is grated water comes out. Do not discard this water; use it in the batter. If the batter is too thick, the vadas come out hard.

Using black gram with skin will increase the nutritive and fibre value.

Remove the skin as follows: After soaking the dal for 3–4 hours, add two cups of water, rub the soaked dal between the palm and fingers of the right hand. Rock the pan to and fro and while doing so pour the water into a second pan. The skins being lighter will fall into the second pan. Remove the skins by decanting the water in the second pan into the first one. Repeat this process till almost all the skin has been removed. The skin can also be removed by adding four cups of water and swirling the soaked dal. Allow it to settle for a minute. Since the skin is lighter it tends to settle on top of the dal. Now remove the skin by hand. Repeat this process till almost all the skin is removed. Use the dal to make vadas and the skin to make dosas.

Dosas made by using the skin: Grind the skin into a fine paste with salt and green chilli. Add whole wheat flour or the ground gram paste itself as required, a few tablespoons of sour curd/lime juice and mix to dosa consistency, using the water in which the black gram was soaked. The dosas may be made immediately without adding curd/lime juice. You may also ferment the batter and make dosas. These dosas will be low in calories.

Do not throw away the leftover water that was used for soaking. Use it to make gravies, soup or for kneading flour for chapatis or for making vegetable dosas. (See p. 199 – Dosas without pulses/non-protein dosas.)

(iii) Ash Gourd Aviyal (6 servings)

See Aviyal on p. 60, 61. [Approx. 50 cal/serving]

2. Banana Stem

Vitamins:
Vitamin A: —
Vitamin B group: low
Vitamin C: low

Banana stem is good for digestive and urinary disorders. It can break or dissolve stones and is a useful remedy for inflammations, burns and cuts.

Cutting banana stem:

Banana stem has a very high fibre content and needs to be cut with care. Cut the stem into thin circular slices. Each time a ring is cut, wind the fibrous thread that comes out on your forefinger. When half a dozen rings have been cut in ths way, place them one on top of the other, cut across horizontally and vertically to get 1–2 mm cubes.

(i) Banana Stem with Curd (4 servings)

Ingredients	Quantity
Banana stem (finely chopped)	1 cup
Freshly set curd	2 cups
Turmeric powder	a pinch
Salt	to taste
Coriander leaves (finely chopped)	2 tbsp
Fresh coconut (grated)	1 tbsp
Seasoning	
Oil	½ tsp
Split black gram	1 tsp
Mustard	½ tsp
Cumin	¼ tsp
Asafoetida	a pinch
Green chilli paste	½ tsp
Onion (finely chopped)	½ cup
Curry leaves	6

Method

1. Add turmeric powder, salt, coriander leaves, grated coconut and finely chopped banana stem to curd .
2. Add seasoning. Mix well. [Approx. **75 cal/serving**]

(ii) Banana Stem with Pulses (3 servings)

Ingredients	Quantity
Banana stem (small pieces)	2 cups
Soaked green gram (split with skin/whole)	½ cup
Salt	to taste
Fresh coconut (grated)	1 tbsp
Seasoning	
Oil	½ tsp
Black gram	1 tsp
Mustard	½ tsp
Cumin	¼ tsp
Asafoetida	a pinch
Red chilli	1
Turmeric powder	a pinch
Curry leaves	6–8

Method

1. Pressure cook banana stem and green gram.
2. Season with black gram, mustard, cumin, asafoetida, red chilli, turmeric powder (optional) and curry leaves.
3. Add salt and coconut and mix well. [Approx. 75 cal/serving]

Note: Cooked sprouted green gram (¾ cup) may also be used in addition to the above ingredients.

(iii) Banana Stem with Sweet and Sour Gravy

See pumpkin recipe (p. 165) in this Chapter. Use 2 cups of raw finely cut pieces of banana stem instead of pumpkin. Mix with coarsely mashed (½ to 1 cup) baked brinjal (if desired) in order to bind the gravy and also for a blended taste.

(iv) Banana Stem Sweet and Sour (Dry/Wet)

See p. 77, 78 (steamed sour vegetables with ginger paste or mustard paste).

3. Beetroot

	Tuber	Leaves
Vitamins		
Vitamin A:	high	high
Vitamin B:	moderate	high
Vitamin C:	low	moderate

Beetroot is rich in minerals like calcium and iron. It is a diuretic, good for the spleen and liver, and for relieving constipation, arthritis and anaemia.

(i) Beetroot Aviyal (5 servings)

Ingredients		Quantity
Beetroot (coarsely grated)		½ kg
Water		½ cup
Salt		to taste
Fresh coconut (grated)	⎫	2 tbsp
Cumin	⎪	¼ tsp
Green chilli	⎬ ground to a paste	3
Onion (finely chopped)	⎪	½ cup
sour or fresh curd	⎭	1 cup
coconut oil		1 tsp

Method

1. Boil beetroot in water.
2. Add salt and ground paste.
3. Boil once.
4. Remove from fire, add coconut oil (optional) and mix. [Approx. 76 cal/serving]

(ii) Beetroot leaves in combination with spinach (dal/pulusu)

See Spinach dal recipes on pp. 169.

4. Bitter Gourd

Vitamins
Vitamin A: moderate
Vitamin B group: moderate
Vitamin C: moderate

Bitter gourd is alkaline in nature. It has been proved that it contains a substance which resembles insulin (a hormone) which lowers sugar levels in the blood and in urine. The cooked vegetable loses its curative properties and is therefore best used raw in the form of juice. This is curative for diabetes, jaundice, rheumatism, asthma and spleen and liver disorders.

(i) Bitter Gourd with Curd (5 servings)

Ingredients	Quantity
Bitter gourd (1 cm cubes)	¼ kg
Salt	2 tsp
Water	½ cup
Oil	1 tbsp
Onion (thick long slices)	1 cup
Turmeric powder	¼ tsp
Red chilli powder	½ tsp
Coriander seed powder	½ tsp
Aniseeds ⎫ powdered	1 tsp
Fenugreek ⎬ coarsely	¼ tsp
Onion seed ⎭	½ tsp
curd	½ cup

Method

1. Smear the whole bitter gourd with salt and set aside for 20 minutes. Then wash, cut and steam it in a pressure cooker for ½ minute with water. Fry in a *kadai* or in a non-stick pan with oil.
2. Add onion, cover *kadai* with a lid and fry for 5 minutes on low flame.
3. Mix turmeric powder, red chilli powder, coriander seed powder and salt to taste.
4. Add powder of aniseed, fenugreek and onion seed, and curd and cook for 5 minutes on low flame. [Approx. **49 cal/serving**]

(ii) Bitter Gourd with Jaggery and Tamarind (Sweet and Sour) (8 servings)

Ingredients	Quantity
Bitter gourd (1" round pieces)	¼ kg.
Salt	to taste

Ingredients	Quantity
Turmeric powder	a pinch
Jaggery	1 lime-size
Thick tamarind extract	2 tbsp
Water	½ cup
Seasoning	
Oil	1 tbsp
Bengal gram	1 tbsp
Black gram	1 tsp
Mustard	1 tsp
Fenugreek	¼ tsp
Asafoetida	a pinch
Red chilli powder	1 tsp

Method

1. To the seasoning, add vegetable, salt, turmeric powder, jaggery, thick tamarind extract, water and cook on low fire till done and almost dry. [Approx. 56 **cal/serving**]

(iii) Bitter Gourd with Tamarind Gravy

Ingredients	Quantity
Bitter gourd (1 cm round pieces)	1 cup
Thick tamarind extract	1 tbsp
Water	1½ cups
Jaggery	1 lime-sized ball
Red chilli powder	1 tsp
Turmeric powder	a pinch
Salt	to taste
Seasonings	
Oil	1 tbsp
Fenugreek	¼ tsp
Mustard	½ tsp
Cumin	¼ tsp
Asafoetida	a pinch

Method

1. To the seasoning, add bitter gourd and fry on low flame till the pieces of vegetable soften a little.
2. Add thick tamarind extract, water, jaggery, red chilli powder, turmeric powder, salt and cook on slow fire.

Bottle Gourd

Vitamins
Vitamin A: —
Vitamin B group: moderate
Vitamin C: low

Cooked bottle gourd is very easy to digest. It is also very useful for urinary disorders because it acts as an alkaline diuretic. It is very useful in summer as it quenches thirst, prevents the loss of sodium, and thus prevent fatigue. It gives vigour, controls coughing and the secretion of bile. Bottle gourd soup is very beneficial in jaundice; fresh juice helps in diabetes, peptic ulcers, high blood pressure and heart ailments. It is very good for indigestion and chronic constipation. The peel contains large amounts of potassium and is beneficial in urinary problems and dysentery.

(i) Bottle Gourd Sweet Curry with Milk and Jaggery

Ingredients	Quantity
Bottle gourd (I cm cubes)	½ kg
Jaggery	1 lime-sized ball
Salt	to taste
Whole wheat flour or rice flour	3 tsp
Milk	1 cup
Seasoning	
Oil or ghee	½ tsp
Black gram	1 tsp
Cumin	¼ tsp
Asafoetida	a pinch
Curry leaves	6–8
Red chilli (pieces)	2–3

Method

1. Steam or boil bottle gourd.
2. Add jaggery, salt and a slurry of whole wheat flour or rice flour in milk. Cook for a few minutes till the flour is cooked.
3. Season with black gram, cumin, asafoetida, curry leaves and pieces of red chilli. [Approx. **55 cal/serving**]

(ii) Bottle Gourd with Pulses (Dals)—Maharashtrian Style

Ingredients	Quantity
Bottle gourd (grated)	½ kg
Bengal gram (soaked)	¼ cup
Water	½ cup
Fresh coconut (grated)	1 tbsp
Coriander leaves (finely chopped)	½ cup
Green chillies (ground)	2
Salt	to taste
Jaggery (optional)	½ tsp powder or bits
Roasted groundnuts with skin (powdered)	1 tbsp
Seasoning	
Oil	½ tsp
Mustard	½ tsp
Asafoetida	a pinch
Curry leaves	4–6

Method

1. Cook grated bottle gourd and presoaked Bengal gram in water.
2. Add a paste of grated coconut, coriander leaves, green chilli, salt and jaggery.
3. Add powder of roasted groundnuts.
4. Season with mustard, asafoetida and curry leaves. [Approx. 65 cal/serving]

(iii) Bottle Gourd Fry

Ingredients	Quantity
Bottle gourd (with peel, pierced 1" cubes)	½ kg
Oil	1 tsp
Salt	to taste
Red chilli powder	to taste

Method

1. Pierce holes in the unpeeled whole gourd with a fork. The fork should also reach the centre of the gourd.
2. Cut into 1" and steam or cook in minimum water.
3. In a *kadai* add oil, gourd, salt and red chilli powder and fry

till the mixture becomes light brown. Alternatively, grease a hot *tava* with ½ tsp oil, add the boiled pieces of vegetable and roast till brown.
4. Turn them over and again add a few drops of oil. [Approx. **28 cal/serving**]

Note: If the vegetable is not tender, remove the peel. Use the peel for making chutney (p. 244) or dosas (p. 198–99)

(iv) Bottle Gourd with Groundnut Powder

Ingredients	Quantity
Bottle gourd (I cm cubes)	½ kg
Turmeric powder	a pinch
Salt	to taste
Roasted groundnut with skin (powdered)	1 tbsp
Seasoning	
Oil	1 tsp
Cumin	½ tsp
Green chilli (slit)	2

Method

1. To the seasoning, add steamed botter gourd, turmeric powder, salt and groundnut powder and mix.
2. Keep on fire for a minute or two. [Approx. **30 cal/serving**]

(v) Bottle Gourd Peel and Seed Chutney

See p. 244.

(vi) Bottle Gourd/Bottle Gourd Peel and Seed Dosas and Pulusu (p. 58)

See pp. 198, 199.

Brinjal

Vitamins
Vitamin A: low
Vitamin B group: high
Vitamin C: low

Brinjal comes in various shapes and colours: round, elongated, big, small, purple, white and green. Green brinjal is said to produce acidity in the body. Purple brinjal is good for the liver. It prevents abortions and is useful in sterility.

Notes: a) Do not cook or serve brinjal in iron pans as the brinjal then turns black. b) When cooking brinjal, use high heat initially.

(i) Brinjal with Sprouted Bengal Gram

Ingredients	Quantity
Brinjal (1" cubes)	½ kg
Bengal gram (sprouted) or	½ cup
Beans seed	
Salt	to taste
Seasoning	
Oil	½ tsp
Black gram	½ tsp
Mustard	½ tsp
Cumin	¼ tsp
Onion (chopped, optional)	½ cup
Green chilli paste	to taste
Ginger paste	to taste
Curry leaves	6
Turmeric powder	a pinch

Method

1. Cook brinjal and sprouted Bengal gram in just enough water needed to cook it.
2. Add salt and season. [Approx. **56 cal/serving**]

(ii) Brinjal with Bottle Gourd/Cauliflower/Cabbage/Beans

Cook the vegetables together as in (i) above and then follow the same procedure, adding tomato if desired. [Approx. **45 cal/serving**]

(iii) Baked Brinjal (Iguru Pachadi)

Ingredients	Quantity
Brinjal	½ kg
Seasoning	
Oil	1 tsp

Ingredients	Quantity
Black gram	1 tsp
Cumin	1 tsp
Green chilli	2
Onion (finely chopped)	1 cup
Salt	to taste

Method

1. Bake and peel brinjal.
2. Add seasoning and mix well. [Approx. **37 cal/serving**]

(iv) Baked Brinjal – Sour Chutney (Banda Pachadi)

Ingredients	Quantity
Brinjal (baked and mashed)	1 cup
Tamarind (washed)	half a lime-sized ball
Onion (1 cm cubes)	¾ cup
Salt	to taste
Turmeric powder	a pinch
Seasoning	
Oil	½ tsp
Black gram	1 tsp
Mustard	½ tsp
Green chilli	3

Method

1. Coarsely pound seasoning of black gram, mustard, green chilli. Add tamarind, onion, salt, turmeric powder and pound again.
2. Add baked brinjal, pound once again and mix thoroughly.
3. While pounding some coriander leaves may be added, for extra flavour. [Approx. **25 cal/serving**]

(v) Baked Brinjals – Sour Gravy Curry (Pulusu Pachadi) (3 servings)

Ingredients	Quantity
Brinjal (baked and mashed)	1 cup
Water	2 cups
Tamarind	half a lime-sized ball
Turmeric powder	a pinch

Ingredients	Quantity
Coriander leaves (finely chopped)	1 tbsp
Tomato (1 cm cubes)	1 cup
Salt	to taste
Seasoning	
Oil	½ tsp
Black gram	½ tsp
Mustard	¼ tsp
Cumin	¼ tsp
Asafoetida	a pinch
Curry leaves	4–6
Red chilli	1
Green chilli paste	½ tsp
Onion (chopped)	½ cup

Method

1. Bake and mash brinjal. Add seasoning.
2. Add water, tamarind extract, turmeric powder, coriander leaves. Mix well and mash.
3. Instead of tamarind, pieces of uncooked ripe tomato can be used. Alternatively a combination of chopped tomato and tamarind extract can also be used. [Approx. **55 cal/serving**]

(vi) Brinjal Gravy Curry with Tomato

Ingredients	Quantity
Brinjal (1 cm cubes)	½ kg
Water	2 cups
Tomato (1 cm cubes)	2 cups
Salt	to taste
Seasoning	
Oil	½ tsp
Black gram	1 tsp
Mustard	½ tsp
Asafoetida	1 pinch
Green chilli	1 or 2
Onion (finely chopped)	½ cup

Method

1. Put seasoning into a *kadai*, add water and boil.

2. Add pieces of brinjal. When half-cooked, add tomato, cook till done and add salt. [Approx. **40 cal/serving**]

(vii) *Traditional Andhra Dish—Brinjal with Curry Powder*

Ingredients	Quantity
Brinjal (1" long pieces)	½ kg
Water	½ cup
For curry powder	
Oil	1 tsp
Bengal gram	2 tbsp
Black gram	2 tbsp
Coriander seed	¼ tsp
Red chilli	2
Cumin	¼ tsp
Asafoetida	a pinch

Method

1. Roast the coriander seed, Bengal gram, black gram, red chilles, cumin and asafoetida in oil till they turn light brown, and powder coarsely.
2. To hot boiling water in a *kadai* add brinjal. Cover *kadai* with a lid on which water is poured. Cook on high flame till brinjal gets well-heated (1–2 minutes).
3. Lower the heat and when brinjal is half-done add the above powder, and salt and mix well.
4. Continue cooking on low fire till almost done.
5. Remove the lid and keep on low fire for a few more minutes. [Approx. **21 cal/serving**]

This dish has the traditional taste as well as the additional advantage of not being oily.

Cabbage

Vitamins
Vitamin A: high
Vitamin B group: moderate
Vitamin C: high

Cabbage is rich in alkaline salts and vitamins. These help to maintain the alkalinity of blood. It also provides fibre. It is a very popular vegetable all over the world. It cures gastric ulcers, hepatitis, jaundice, bleeding gums, piles and urinary ailments. It is useful in treating skin diseases and blood disorders, diabetes, pulmonary complaints and rheumatism (due to its sulphur content).

(i) Cabbage with Raw Additives

Ingredients	Quantity
Cabbage (finely chopped)	½ kg
Water	2 cups
Turmeric powder	a pinch
Salt	to taste
Fresh coconut (grated)	1 tbsp
Coriander leaves (finely chopped)	1 cup
Ginger	½" piece
Garlic (flakes)	2–3
Onion (finely chopped)	¼–½ cup
Green chilli	1
Tomato (finely cut)	¼–½ cup
Seasoning	
Oil	½–1 tsp
Black gram	1 tsp
Mustard	½ tsp
Red chilli	1
Curry leaves	6–8

Method

1. Boil cabbage in water.
2. Add turmeric powder, salt and a paste of coconut, coriander leaves, ginger, garlic, onion, green chilli and tomatoes.
3. Season and serve. [Approx. 58 **cal/serving**]

(ii) Cabbage with Garlic

Ingredients	Quantity
Cabbage (finely chopped)	½ kg
Water	½ cup

Ingredients	Quantity
Seasoning	
Oil	1 tsp
Garlic (crushed)	1 tbsp
Red chilli powder	½ tsp
Salt	to taste

Method

1. Heat oil in a pan and add seasoning.
2. Add cabbage and water, and cook on low flame till done. [Approx. 35 cal/serving]

(iii) Cabbage Kofta Curry (made without deep frying)

Ingredients	Quantity
Cooked rice	1 cup
Cabbage (finely chopped/grated)	2 cups
Chapati (fresh or leftover) (torn into small pieces)	1 cup
Whole wheat flour	½ cup
Ginger–garlic–green chilli paste	1 tsp
Coriander–cumin seed powder	1 tsp
Salt	to taste
Red chilli powder	½ tsp
Water (if needed)	
Any North Indian gravy	

Method

1. Mix cooked rice, cabbage, chapati, whole wheat flour, ginger–garlic–green chilli paste, coriander–cumin seed powder, salt, red chilli powder together (using water if needed).
2. Mix well and roll into lemon-sized balls.
3. Boil 4–5 cups of water to which a little salt has been added.
4. Add cabbage balls and let them simmer for 10–15 minutes till they get cooked.
5. Remove from fire and drain immediately.
6. Add these koftas to any gravy made with the drained water. Boil once.
7. If required, mash one ball to add thickness to the gravy. If necessary, add 1 tbsp beaten cream or a fine paste made from

a few cashewnuts/groundnuts or khus khus in milk. [Approx. 48 cal/serving]

(iv) Cabbage Snack

Ingredients	Quantity
Cabbage Koftas (see Recipe (iii) above)	
Seasoning	
Oil	1 tsp
Mustard	½ tsp
Cumin	¼ tsp
Green chilli bits	½ tsp
Turmeric powder	a pinch
Red chilli powder	½ tsp
Garam masala powder	a pinch
Dry mango powder/thick tamarind extract	½ tsp
Coriander seed powder	½ tsp
Onion (finely chopped)	½–1 cup
Garnishing	
Coriander leaves (finely chopped)	1–2 tbsp

Method

1. Add seasoning to the koftas.
2. Mix well and garnish with coriander leaves. [Approx. 40 cal/serving]

Note: Do not throw away the inner edible portion and outer green leaves of cabbage as they are also rich in nutrients and fibre. They can be used for the recipes given on pp. 122–23.

Capsicum

Vitamins
Vitamin A: high
Vitamin B group: moderate
Vitamin C: high

(i) Capsicum with Gram Flour (Besan)

Ingredients	Quantity
Capsicum (1 cm squares)	½ kg

Ingredients	Quantity
Turmeric powder	¼ tsp
Red chilli powder	1 tsp
Gram flour	1 cup
Seasoning	
Oil	2 tsp
Mustard	½ tsp
Asafoetida	a pinch

Method

1. Season mustard and asafoetida, and add capsicum.
2. Mix and cover the pan with a lid.
3. When almost cooked, add salt, turmeric powder, red chilli powder and gram flour.
4. Mix well and fry till done without covering, stirring frequently to avoid charring.
5. Sprinkle a little water if necessary, to avoid capsicum becoming too dry. [Approx. **71 cal/serving**]

Notes: (a) To use minimum oil for frying, put water on lid of pan, and cook till almost done. Then fry uncovered to get a fried taste. (b) Instead of gram flour, whole wheat flour or a mixture of whole wheat flour and rice flour may also be used.

(ii) Capsicum with Tomato and Onion Stuffing

Ingredients	Quantity
Capsicums	½ kg
Oil	1 tsp
Onion (grated)	1 cup
Tomato (1" cubes, 1 piece for each capsicum and 6 more over and above this)	
Water	

Method

1. Slit capsicums into 4 leaving the base intact (without fully cutting into separate pieces).
2. Fry grated onion, add tomato, turmeric powder, salt, red chilli powder (to taste) and fry till the pieces of tomato soften.

3. Use this to stuff each capsicum.
4. Place stuffed capsicum in a *kadai*, add oil, the leftover stuffing and 1 tbsp water.
5. Cover with a lid till cooked. Pour water on top of the lid to minimise the amount of oil needed to cook the vegetable. [Approx. **40 cal/serving**]

(iii) Capsicum with Groundnut Powder

Ingredients	Quantity
Capsicum (1 cm squares)	4 cups
Potato (1 cm cubes)	1 cup
Coriander–cumin powder	1 tsp
Red chilli powder	to taste
Roasted groundnuts with skin (powdered)	1 tbsp
Salt	to taste
Seasoning	
Oil	1 tbsp
Mustard	1 tsp
Cumin	½ tsp
Asafoetida	a pinch
Onion (roughly chopped)	1 cup

Method

1. Fry capsicum and potato with seasoning.
2. When done, add coriander–cumin seed powder, red chilli powder, powdered roasted groundnuts, and salt and mix well. [Approx. **56 cal/serving**]

Carrot

Vitamins
Vitamin A: very high
Vitamin B group: moderate
Vitamin C: low

Carrot is strongly alkaline and rich in minerals (chlorine, magnesium and silicon, calcium, iron and phosphorus). Carrot contains ten times more beta-carotene (a precursor of vitamin A). than cow milk. Carrot strengthens eyes, nerves and keeps the mucous membranes in all parts of the body healthy. It guards against infections (antiseptic properties), and is good for gout and liver.

Carrot Koshimbir

Ingredients	Quantity
Carrot (grated)	½ kg
Salt	to taste
roasted groundnuts with skin (powdered)	2 tsp
Fresh coconut (grated)	4 tsp
Coriander leaves (finely chopped)	1–2 tsp
Seasoning	
Ghee	½ tsp
Mustard	½ tsp
Asafoetida	a pinch
Green chilli (pieces)	2
Curry leaves	6–8

Method

1. Grate carrot, add salt, roasted groundnut powder, coconut, coriander leaves and season.
2. Mix well.
3. Instead of using raw grated carrot, the grated carrot can be cooked for just a minute or two, sprinkled with a little water to soften it, a little after adding the seasoning. Add groundnut, coriander and coconut and mix. Soaked/sprouted green gram (2–3 tbsp) can also be added. [Approx. 55 **cal/serving**]

Cauliflower

Vitamins
Vitamin A: low
Vitamin B group: high
Vitamin C: moderate

Cauliflower is very good for pregnant women. Raw cauliflower may cure peptic ulcers if taken regularly. It should not be taken by those suffering from goitre.

(i) Cauliflower (large florets)—Steamed and Fried

Ingredients	Quantity
Cauliflower (large florets)	½ kg
Red chilli powder	1 tsp
Salt	to taste
Oil	1 tsp

Method

1. Lightly steam cauliflower florets.
2. Put 1 tsp oil into a greased *kadai* and fry cauliflower with salt and red chilli powder. [Approx. **34 cal/serving**]

(ii) Cauliflower with Tomato

Ingredients	Quantity
Cauliflower (large florets)	½ kg
Water	2 cups
Oil	2 tsp
Onion (grated)	1 tbsp
Ginger–garlic paste	1 tbsp
Tomato (crushed)	1½ cups
Sugar	1 tsp
Red chilli powder	½ tsp
Dry fenugreek leaves (optional)	1 tsp
Salt	to taste
Milk	1 tbsp

Method

1. Boil cauliflower florets for 2–3 minutes in boiling water and drain (use this water for soups or gravies) or cook on low fire in just ½ cup water and set aside.
2. Heat oil in a non-stick pan or *kadai*. Add grated onion, ginger–garlic paste and fry till brown.
3. Add crushed tomato, sugar, red chilli powder, fenugreek leaves and salt.
4. Cook for 5–6 minutes on low fire.
5. Add cooked cauliflower, cover with a lid, cook for a minute and add milk. [Approx. **50 cal/serving**]

Note: Do not throw away the tender leaves with stalks and edible inner white portion of the stem as these also are rich in nutrients and fibre. Cut them into small pieces. Steam cook or cook with minimum oil along with finely chopped potato/peas/carrot/beans etc. These stalks can be used in the various ways given below:

(a) Dry Curry

Ingredients	Quantity
Cauliflower stalks	2 cups
Salt	to taste
Coriander leaves (garnishing)	1 tbsp
Fresh coconut (grated)	1 tbsp
Salt	to taste
Seasoning	
Oil	1 tsp
Bengal gram	1 tsp
Black gram	1 tsp
Mustard	½ tsp
Green chilli paste	1 tsp
Ginger paste	1 tsp
Curry leaves	10
Onion (finely chopped, optional)	½–1 cup

Method

1. To the seasoning, add cooked cauliflower stalks and salt. Mix well and remove from fire.
2. Garnish with coriander leaves and fresh grated coconut.

(b) Gravy Curry

This can be added to any of the gravies described on pp. 54–58, 66–69.

(c) As Upma

See Semolina snacks on pp. 215–17.

(d) Dosas with Grated Cauliflower Stalks

Grate the stalks and make whole wheat flour vegetable dosas (see pp. 198, 199, 203).

(e) Chutney with Cauliflower Stalks and Leaves

Follow the same procedure as for Tomato/Vegetable Peel Chutney (see pp. 243, 244).

Chow Chow Marrow (Bangalore Brinjal, Cho-Cho)

Vitamins
Vitamin A:
Vitamin B group: low
Vitamin C: low

This vegetable is good for people with diabetes and for weak children.

(i) Chow Chow Marrow with Coriander Leaves

Ingredients		Quantity
Chow chow marrow (1 cm pieces)		½ kg
Fresh coconut (grated)		1 tsp
Coriander leaves (finely chopped)		½ cup
Garlic		1 or 2 flakes
Green chilli	ground to a paste	1
Ginger		½" piece
Salt		to taste
Amchur/raw mango/tamarind		little

Method

1. Steam vegetable with minimum water.
2. To the paste add steamed marrow and cook for a minute. [Approx. 36 cal/serving]

(ii) Chow Chow Marrow with Curd and Mustard

Ingredients	Quantity
Chow chow marrow (1 cm cubes)	½ kg
Fresh coconut (grated)	1 tbsp
Green chilli	1
Mustard seed	1 tsp
Salt	to taste
curd	2 cups

Ingredients	Quantity
Seasoning	
Oil	1 tsp
Mustard seed	½ tsp
Curry leaves	4–6

Method

1. To the marrow cooked in minimum water, add the paste of coconut, green chilli, mustard, salt and curd.
2. Boil once and season. Mash the vegetable a little. [Approx. 55 cal/serving]

(iii) Chow Chow with Gravy

See pp. 62–64.

Cluster Beans

Vitamins
Vitamin A: moderate
Vitamin B group: moderate
Vitamin C: moderate

(i) Cluster Beans with Thyme (Ajwain) (7 servings)

Ingredients	Quantity
Cluster beans (1" pieces)	½ kg
Pumpkin (1" cubes)	¼ kg
Water	2 tbsp
Seasoning	
Thyme (ajwain)	1 tsp
Red chilli	1 or 2
Turmeric powder	a pinch
Curry leaves	6–8
Coriander–cumin seed powder	1 tsp

Method

1. Cook the cluster beans and pumpkin in water.
2. Season with thyme, red chilli, turmeric powder, curry leaves and coriander–cumin seed powder.

3. Add salt, mix well and leave on fire for 1–2 minutes. [Approx. 25 cal/serving]

(ii) Cluster Beans with Coconut Paste

Ingredients		Quantity
Cluster beans (1 cm pieces)		½ kg.
Water		2 tbsp
Fresh coconut (grated)	} ground to a paste	1 tbsp
Green chilli		2
roasted groundnuts with skin (powdered)		1 tbsp
Seasoning		
Oil		1 tsp
Black gram		1 tsp
Mustard		¼ tsp
Curry leaves		6–8

Method

1. Cook beans in water.
2. Add the paste and salt.
3. Season and serve. [Approx. **30 cal/serving**]

(iii) Cluster Beans in Sour Gravy with Coconut

Ingredients	Quantity
Cluster beans (1 cm pieces)	½ kg
Water	1 cup
Salt	to taste
Lemon juice/raw mango (grated)/ thick tamarind extract	1–2 tsp
Fresh coconut (grated)	1 tbsp
Green chilli	2
Ginger	½" piece
Garlic (fried)	4 flakes
Coriander seed	1 tsp
Cumin	1 tsp
Jaggery	to taste
slurry of whole wheat flour	2 tsp
Water	4 tbsp

Ingredients	Quantity
Seasoning	
Oil	1 tsp
Black gram	1 tsp
Mustard	¼ tsp
Curry leaves	6–8
Red/green chilli (pieces)	to taste

Method

1. Cook the bean in water.
2. Add salt, lemon juice/raw mango/tamarind paste, jaggery and the slurry of whole wheat flour.
3. Grind coconut, green chillies, ginger, garlic, roasted coriander seeds and roasted cumin together.
4. Add this to the beans and season with black gram, mustard, curry leaves and red/green chilli. [Approx. **48 cal/serving**]

(iv) Cluster Beans with Coriander Leaves

Ingredients	Quantity
Cluster beans (1 cm pieces)	¼ kg
Salt	to taste
Turmeric powder	a pinch
Tomato (finely chopped)	¼ cup
Coriander leaves (finely chopped)	½ cup
Seasoning	
Oil	1 tsp
Black gram	1 tsp
Mustard	½ tsp
Cumin	¼ tsp
Curry leaves	4–6
Onion (finely chopped)	¼ cup
Asafoetida	a pinch
Green chilli or red chilli powder	to taste

Method

1. Steam beans without water.
2. Add salt, turmeric powder, tomato, coriander leaves and

seasoning of black gram, mustard, cumin, curry leaves, onion, or asafoetida, green chilli paste or red chilli powder.

3. Mash till tomato also get slightly mashed. [Approx. 35 cal/serving]

Note: If tomato is not available, use grated or pounded raw mango, or tamarind extract.

(v) Cluster Beans (Sweet and Sour)

See p. 78.

Colocasia

Vitamins
Vitamin A: low
Vitamin B group: moderate
Vitamin C:

Colocasia acts as a nerve tonic. It helps in increasing body weight. It is useful in hemorrhoids.

(i) Colocasia—Sour and Dry (2 servings)

Ingredients	Quantity
Colocasia (1" round pieces) (boiled)	10–14
Turmeric powder	¼ tsp
Salt	to taste
Thick tamarind extract	½ tsp
or	
Raw mango (grated)	¼ cup
Seasoning	
Oil	1 tsp
Black gram	1 tsp
Mustard	½ tsp
Curry leaves	6–8
Onion (1" long slices)	1 cup
Red chilli	2

Method

1. To the seasoning, add preboiled colocasia, turmeric powder, salt and tamarind extract (or raw mango).

2. Fry for some time stirring intermittently. [Approx. **130** cal/serving]

(ii) Colocasia with Curd (3 servings)

Ingredients	Quantity
Colocasia (½" pieces) (boiled and peeled)	2 cups
Salt	to taste
Water	½ cup
Curd	1 tbsp
Seasoning	
Oil	1 tsp
Thyme	½ tsp
Crushed garlic	1 tsp
Turmeric powder	¼ tsp
Coriander seed powder	1 tsp
Chilli powder	½ tsp

Method

1. Boil, peel and cut colocasia.
2. Add to the seasoning.
3. Add salt and water and boil for a few minutes.
4. Add curd and remove from fire after one minute. [Approx. 97 cal/serving]

(iii) Colocasia Cutlets (3 servings)

Ingredients	Quantity
Colocasia	¼ kg
Ginger (grated)	1 tbsp
Coriander leaves (finely chopped)	1 tbsp
Green chilli (finely chopped)	1 tsp
Carrot (grated)	1 cup
Pepper powder	½ tsp
Bread crumbs (optional)	2 tbsp
Salt	to taste

Method

1. Boil, peel and mash colocasia.
2. Add ginger, coriander leaves, green chilli, carrot, pepper powder, bread crumbs and salt.

3. Divide into 1½" diameter balls and flatten them to give the desired cutlet shape.
4. Shallow fry on greased *tava*.
5. Serve with any chutney or tomato sauce. [Approx. **110 cal/ serving**]

Colocasia Leaves

Vitamins
Vitamin A: very high
Vitamin B group: high
Vitamin C: high

Colocasia leaves are helpful in scanty urination and are a very good source of vitamin A.

(i) Colocasia Leaves – Sweet and Sour Gravy (5 servings)

Ingredients	Quantity
Colocasia leaves with stalks (10–12)	¼ kg
Groundnuts with skin (presoaked)	24
Green chilli	1
Water	1 cup
Thick tamarind extract/fine paste of raw mango	1 tbsp
Jaggery	1 lime-sized ball
Turmeric powder	a pinch
Slurry of any flour (I tsp) in water (2 tbsp)	
Fresh coconut (grated)	1 tbsp
Seasoning	
Oil	½ tsp
Mustard	½ tsp
Asafoetida	a pinch
Curry leaves	6–8

Method

1. Wash and chop leaves finely.
2. Peel/scale the outer fibrous layer of the stalks of the leaves and then chop them finely.
3. Pressure cook or steam the leaves and stalks together.

4. Add groundnuts, green chilli and water.
5. Add tamarind extract (or raw mango), jaggery, turmeric powder, slurry and coconut.
6. Boil once or twice and then season. [Approx. **88 cal/serving**]

Notes: a) Groundnuts may be crushed a little. b) Pre-soaked split Bengal gram (chana dal) can be used instead of groundnuts. c) Maharashtrian kala masala powder (1 tsp) may also be added.

(ii) Colocasia Leaf Vadas

Ingredients	Quantity
Colocasia leaves	2
Fresh coconut (grated)	1 tbsp
Turmeric powder	$\frac{1}{4}$ tsp
Bengal gram flour	2 tbsp
Asafoetida	a pinch
Red chilli powder	1 tsp
Thick tamarind extract (optional)	$\frac{1}{2}$ tsp
Salt	to taste

Method

1. Cut the stalks off the leaves and use only the leaves.
2. Make a thick paste of coconut, turmeric powder, Bengal gram flour, asafoetida, red chilli powder, thick tamarind extract and salt.
3. Smear one side of each leaf with this paste.
4. Roll the leaf into a cylinder and repeat the process for all the leaves and steam them in a pan for 20 minutes.
5. Cut into 2" long pieces and serve.
6. If a slightly fried taste is desired, place the pieces on a hot greased *tava*. After one side is roasted turn them over and roast again for a while. The pieces can also be deep fried. Serve hot with any chutney. [Approx. **80 cal/serving**]

Note: a) The steamed pieces of leaves can be added to north Indian gravy masala for a gravy dish. b) Instead of Bengal gram flour, a combination of Bengal gram flour, rice flour and/or whole wheat flour or black gram paste can be used.

Corn (Fresh)

Vitamins
Vitamin A: low
Vitamin B group: low
Vitamin C: low

Corn has a high fibre content and its milk is easily digestible.

(i) Fresh Corn with Simple Seasoning (2 servings)

Ingredients	Quantity
Corn	2 cobs
Coriander leaves (finely chopped)	1–2 tbsp
Fresh coconut (grated)	1–2 tbsp
Seasoning	
Oil	1 tsp
Black gram	1 tsp
Mustard	½ tsp
Cumin	¼ tsp
Asafoetida	a pinch
Red/green chilli	1
Curry leaves	6–8
Onion (finely chopped)	½ cup

Method

1. Cook corn in a pressure cooker and grate. or
   Remove the pearls and then coarsely grind.
2. To the seasoning add the cooked corn and salt.
3. Garnish with coriander leaves and coconut. [Approx. **135 cal/
   serving**]

Note: Instead of boiling the corn and then grating it, the uncooked
corn can be grated, if it is reasonably tender. Add this grated corn
into the seasoning, mix and cover. Keep on low fire for a few
minutes till the corn is cooked. Add salt and mix. Garnish with
coriander leaves and coconut (1–2 tbsp of each).

(ii) Fresh Corn Pulusu Pachadi

Ingredients	Quantity
Thick tamarind extract	2 tsp
Jaggery	1 small lime-size ball
Turmeric powder	a pinch
Water	1 to 1½ cups
Baked brinjal (optional)	½ to 1 cup pulp

Method

1. To the corn dish (given in **recipe (i)** add thick tamarind extract, jaggery, turmeric powder, and water and mix well.
2. Add pulp of baked brinjal for binding (optional).

(iii) Fresh Corn Raita

See Boiled Vegetable Raita on p. 247.

Cucumber

Vitamins
Vitamin A: —
Vitamin B group: low
Vitamin C: low

Cucumber is cooling, alkaline, helps in rheumatism, is good for urine troubles and for those who want to lose weight. It also possesses insulin-like properties.

(i) Cucumber Koshimbir

Ingredients	Quantity
Cucumber	½ kg
Salt	to taste
Roasted groundnuts with skin (powdered)	2 tbsp
Fresh coconut (grated)	2 tbsp
Coriander leaves (finely chopped)	½ cup
Seasoning	
Oil	½ tsp
Mustard	½ tsp
Cumin	¼ tsp

Ingredients	Quantity
Asafoetida	a pinch
Green chilli (pieces or paste)	1 tsp
Curry leaves	6–8

Method

1. Grate cucumber.
2. Add salt, roasted groundnut powder, coconut, coriander leaves and seasoning and mix well.
3. Instead of groundnut powder, pre-soaked split green gram with skin or sprouts of green gram or Bengal gram and lime juice can be added. [Approx. **58 cal/serving**]

(ii) Cucumber with Pulses

See Dal recipes on pp. 56 and 255.

(iii) Cucumber Peel Chutney/Dosas

See Vegetable Peel Chutney on pp. 243, 244 and 198, 199.

Drumstick

Vitamins	Vegetable	Leaves
Vitamin A:	moderate	high
Vitamin B group:	low	moderate
Vitamin C:	high	high

Drumstick is very useful for cough, cold, kidney stones, enlargement of liver and spleen, constipation, sciatica, paralysis, flatulence and lumbago. It is also very helpful in removing worms from the digestive system. It is effective against dandruff if applied on the scalp.

(i) Drumstick with Coconut, Milk and Jaggery (3 servings)

Ingredients	Quantity
Drumstick (1½" long pieces)	20
Salt	to taste
Water	½ cup
Jaggery (lime-sized)	2

Ingredients	Quantity
Fresh coconut (grated)	½ cup
Slurry of whole wheat flour/rice flour (¼–½ cup), milk (I cup) and water (2 cups)	
Seasoning	
Oil	½ tsp
Curry leaves	6–8
Asafoetida	a pinch
Cumin	½ tsp
Red chillies	2

Method

1. Cook drumstick with salt (otherwise it may taste bitter), water and jaggery.
2. Add grated coconut, and the slurry.
3. Cook on low fire for a few minutes till the flour is cooked and thickens, adding water if necessary.
4. Season with curry leaves, asafoetida, cumin and red chilli. [Approx. **105 cal/serving**]

(ii) Drumstick with Bengal Gram Flour (7 servings)

Ingredients	Quantity
Bengal gram flour	2 tbsp
Drumstick (2" long pieces)	12
Water	1 cup
Salt	to taste
Seasoning	
Oil	1 tbsp
Mustard	½ tsp
Ginger–garlic paste	1 tbsp
Turmeric powder	¼ tsp
Red chilli powder	½ tsp
Coriander seed powder	1 tsp

Method

1. Dry roast the gram flour and set aside.
2. Heat oil; add mustard, ginger–garlic paste, turmeric powder, red chilli powder and coriander seed powder.

3. Add pieces of the drumstick, water, and salt and cook till done covering the *kadai* with a lid on which water is poured.
4. Add roasted gram flour, stir and cook for 2–3 minutes. [Approx. 87 **cal/serving**]

Fenugreek Leaves

Vitamins
Vitamin A: high
Vitamin B group: high
Vitamin C: moderate

Fresh fenugreek leaves are very beneficial in the treatment of indigestion, flatulence, liver ailments and mouth ulcers. Fenugreek leaves and fenugreek seeds are very effective in diabetes and pain in the joints, and in providing relief from piles.

(i) Fenugreek Leaves with Potato (4 servings)

Ingredients	Quantity
Potato (I cm squares)	1½ cups
Salt	to taste
Fenugreek leaves (finely chopped)	3 cups
Red chilli powder	½ tsp
Seasoning	
Oil	1 tsp
Cumin	¼ tsp
Green chilli	2

Method

1. Heat oil in a pan and add cumin, green chillies and potato.
2. Add salt and cook covering the pan with a lid on which water is poured.
3. When half-done, add fenugreek leaves, and cook till done.
4. Add red chilli powder, if desired, and remove from fire. [Approx. 76 **cal/serving**]

Note: Remove the lid and cook on low fire after the potato and greens are cooked, to give a reasonably fried taste.

(ii) Fenugreek Leaves with Red Gram (Arhar) or Red Gram in combination with Bengal Gram (5 servings)

Ingredients	Quantity
Fenugreek leaves (finely chopped)	3 cups
Tomato (½" pieces)	2 cups
Red chilli powder	1 tsp
Red gram	1 cup
Bengal gram (optional)	½ cup
Fresh coconut (grated)	¼–½ cup
Onion (1" long pieces, optional) (roasted in ½ tsp oil)	1 cup
Salt	to taste
Seasoning	
Oil	1 tsp
Mustard	¼ tsp
Onion (1 cm cubes)	1 cup

Method

1. Add fenugreek leaves and tomato to a seasoning of mustard and onion.
2. Cook till done without adding much water. (The water in the tomato itself is enough for cooking on low fire.)
3. When almost done add salt, red chilli powder and either just cooked red gram or a combination of cooked red gram and Bengal gram, and fresh coconut.
4. Mix well, keep for a minute on fire and remove.
5. Onion fried in ½ tsp oil can be added as garnish for extra flavour. [Approx. 79 cal/serving]

(iii) Fenugreek Leaves with Whole Green Gram (Moong) (3 servings)

Ingredients	Quantity
Whole green gram	1 cup
Fenugreek leaves (finely chopped)	¼ kg
Salt	to taste
Seasoning	
Oil	½ tsp
Mustard	½ tsp

Ingredients	Quantity
Cumin	½ tsp
Red chilli	1 or 2
Curry leaves	6–8
Asafoetida/garlic (chopped/paste)	to taste

Method

1. Cook green gram, add fenugreek leaves and cook till done.
2. Add salt and seasoning. [Approx. **72 cal/serving**]

Note: Soaked green gram (whole/split, with skin or sprouted) may also be used. The amount can be varied according to taste.

(iv) Fenugreek Leaves with Brinjal (4 servings)

Ingredients	Quantity
Brinjal (½" cubes)	½ kg
Water	½ cup
Fenugreek leaves (finely chopped)	2 cups
Salt	to taste
Turmeric powder	a pinch
Seasoning	
Oil	1 tsp
Onion seed	½ tsp
Green chilli	2

Method

1. To the seasoning, add water, brinjal, fenugreek leaves, salt and turmeric powder.
2. Cover the *kadai* with a lid on which water is poured. Leave undisturbed for 5 minutes on medium fire, stir and cook on low fire, sprinkling a little water if necessary. [Approx. **52 cal/serving**]

(v) Fenugreek Leaf Rice

See p. 250.

French Beans

Vitamins
Vitamin A: moderate
Vitamin B group: low
Vitamin C: low

Cooked French beans are good for diarrhoea, dysentery and constipation. They are helpful in typhoid, peptic ulcers and diabetes.

(i) French Beans with Green Coriander Paste (5 servings)

Ingredients		Quantity
French beans (finely chopped)		½ kg
Coriander leaves (finely chopped)		1 cup
Green chilli	ground to	2
Salt	a paste	to taste
Jaggery		½ tsp
Seasoning		
Oil		1 tsp
Black gram		1 tsp
Mustard		½ tsp
Curry leaves		6–8

Method

1. Dry steam the beans.
2. Add the paste.
3. Season with black gram, mustard and curry leaves. [Approx. 44 cal/serving]

(ii) French Beans with raw Onion, Coconut paste (5 servings)

Ingredients		Quantity
French beans (1" long pieces)		½ kg
Fresh coconut (grated)		2 tbsp
Raw onion (1 cm cubes)	ground	¾ cup
Green chilli	coarsely	2
Cumin		1 tsp
Salt		to taste
Coriander leaves (finely chopped, optional)		1–2 tbsp

Method

1. Dry steam the beans.
2. Add the coarse paste.
3. Mix well. Coriander leaves may be added while grinding.
   [Approx. **52 cal/serving**]

(iii) French Beans and Brinjal (9 servings)

Ingredients	Quantity
French beans (1" long pieces)	½ kg
Brinjal (1" cubes/pieces)	½ kg
Salt	to taste
Tomato (1 cm cubes)	½ cup
Green chilli (pieces/paste)	1 tsp
Ginger (pieces/paste)	1 tsp
Seasoning	
Oil	1 tsp
Black gram	1 tsp
Mustard	½ tsp
Red chilli	1
Onion (finely chopped)	½ cup
Curry leaves	6–8

Method

1. Half-cook the beans, add brinjal and cook till both are done.
2. Add salt and seasoning; cook for a few minutes.
3. Add tomato and cook till done.
4. Just before removing from fire add chilli and ginger paste.
   [Approx. **42 cal/serving**]

Flat and Broad Beans

Vitamins
Vitamin A: low
Vitamin B group: moderate
Vitamin C: low

Flat and broad beans prevent hair falling. They are a good sources of protein.

(i) Flat Beans with dry grated Coconut (Kopra)

Ingredients	Quantity
Flat beans (1" long pieces)	½ kg
Potato (1" long slices)	1 cup
Salt	to taste
Red chilli powder	to taste
Curry powder	1 tbsp
Fresh or dry grated coconut	2 tbsp
Salt	to taste
Seasoning	
Oil	1 tsp
Onion (1" long sliced)	½ cup

Method

1. Dry steam beans (without adding water) and potato separately.
2. Lightly fry the onion in oil .
3. Add vegetables; add salt, red chilli powder and curry powder.
4. Cook for a minute and add coconut.
5. Mix well and remove from fire. [Approx. **90 cal/serving**]

(ii) Flat Beans with Curry Powder (5 servings)

Ingredients	Quantity
Flat beans (finely sliced)	4 cups
Fresh coconut (grated)	1–2 tsp
Curry powder	1 tbsp
Salt	to taste
Red chilli powder	to taste
Seasoning	
Oil	1 tsp
Black gram (optional)	1 tsp
Mustard	½ tsp
Curry leaves	6–8

Method

1. Steam beans (without adding water).
2. Add beans, coconut, curry powder, salt and red chilli powder to the seasoning.

3. Mix well, leave on fire for a minute and remove. [Approx. 74 cal/serving]

Goosefoot White

Vitamins
Vitamin A: high
Vitamin B group: moderate
Vitamin C: moderate

This vegetable is a good source of vitamins. It strengthens the heart and helps in purifying blood. It is very helpful in ailments of muscles and ligaments. It is a very good liver tonic and cures constipation.

Sweet and Sour Goosefoot White with Green Gram and Fried Onion

Ingredients	Quantity
goosefoot white leaves (finely cut)	6 cups
Green gram (split with skin or whole)	½ cup
Water	2 cups
Thick tamarind extract	1 tbsp
Jaggery	1 lime-size ball
Salt	to taste
Slurry of whole wheat flour (1 tsp) and water (½ cup)	
Seasoning	
Oil	1 tsp
Fenugreek seed	¼ tsp
Mustard	½ tsp
Onion (1" long slices)	1 cup
Curry leaves	6–8
Asafoetida	a pinch
Green chilli paste	1 tsp

Method

1. Boil leaves and green gram in water.
2. Add thick tamarind extract, jaggery, salt and the slurry of whole wheat flour and boil again.

3. Season with fenugreek seed, mustard, onion, curry leaves, asafoetida and green chilli paste. [Approx. **90 cal/serving**]

Green Peas

Vitamins
Vitamin A: low
Vitamin B group: low
Vitamin C: low

Green peas are a good source of protein, but should not be eaten by those suffering from gout, kidney/gall bladder complaints and arthritis.

(i) Green Peas in-the-pod (3 servings)

Ingredients	Quantity
Green pea shells (finely chopped)	1 cup
Vegetables such as potato,	
Cabbage and any other English vegetables (diced)	1 cup
Water	¼ cup
Jaggery powder (optional)	½ tsp
Red chilli powder	to taste
Salt	to taste
Seasoning	
Oil	1 tsp
Mustard	½ tsp
Cumin	¼ tsp
Asafoetida	a pinch
Onion (optional)	½ cup

Method

1. String the pea pods, and remove the tough cellulose layer of the shell.
2. Chop and add to the seasoning and diced vegetable. Sprinkle water.
3. Cook after covering the *kadai* with a lid on which water is poured.

4. When almost done, add jaggery, red chilli powder and salt to taste. [Approx. 40 cal/serving]

(ii) Green Pea Usal or Amti (4 servings)

Ingredients	Quantity
Shelled peas	2 cups
Water	2 cups
Salt	to taste
Red chilli powder	¼ tsp
Turmeric powder	¼ tsp
Jaggery	to taste
Thick tamarind extract	1 tbsp
Fresh coconut (grated)	1–2 tbsp
Coriander leaves (finely chopped)	½–1 cup
Maharastrian kala masala powder	1 tsp
Seasoning	
Oil	1 tsp
Mustard	½ tsp
Asafoetida	a pinch
Curry leaves	6–8
Onion (finely chopped)	½ cup

Method

1. Boil or steam the shelled peas in water.
2. Add salt, red chilli powder, turmeric powder, jaggery, thick tamarind extract, fresh grated coconut, coriander leaves, Maharashtrian kala masala powder, and seasoning.
3. Heat till the mixture comes to a boil. Mash it a little. [Approx. 55 cal/serving]

Note: Garam masala powder (¼ tsp), coriander seed powder or cumin powder (½ teaspoon) may be substituted for Maharashtrian kala masala powder.

Indian Gooseberry (Amla)

Vitamins
Vitamin A: low
Vitamin B group: low
Vitamin C: very high

Amla has a very high curative and nutritive value, and is the richest source of vitamin C among vegetables. One amla supplies the vitamin C required for a week. The fresh fruit is a light diuretic and laxative. It is a valuable medicine for the treatment of several diseases. It should preferably be eaten fresh but when this is not possible, the dried fruit may be used with good effect as its acidity has a protective action on vitamin C. It gives vigour and strength to the body, purifies blood, increases immunity and is valuable in respiratory disorders (asthma, tuberculosis of the lungs, bronchitis), renal disorders, constipation and dyspepsia. It is the best remedy for scurvy.

(i) Indian Gooseberry Chutney

See p. 239.

(ii) Indian Gooseberry Juice

Ingredients	Quantity
Indian gooseberry	1 or 2
Water	1 cup

Method

1. Finely grate or crush the gooseberry and squeeze out the juice.
2. Dilute it with water and take on an empty stomach. It is an excellent medicine/tonic.

(iii) Indian Gooseberry Pickle

Ingredients	Quantity
Indian gooseberry	250 g
Water	1 cup
Salt	to taste
Seasoning	
Oil	1 tbsp
Aniseed	1 tsp
Turmeric powder	¼ tsp
Red chilli powder	½ tsp

Method

1. Blanch the Indian gooseberries in water. Drain and remove the seeds.
2. Heat oil, add aniseed, turmeric powder, red chilli powder, gooseberries and salt.
3. Cook for 6–7 minutes on low fire and cool.
4. This pickle can be preserved for 15–20 days. Some more oil can be added to preserve it for a longer time. [Approx. **305 cal (total)**]

Note: Do not throw away the water used for blanching the gooseberries. Use it for gravies or drink it as it is.

(iii) Digestive Pills Indian Gooseberry

Ingredients	Quantity
Indian gooseberry	500 g
Cumin powder	1 tsp
Black salt	1 tsp
Salt	to taste

Method

1. Boil gooseberries and remove the seeds.
2. Mash well and add cumin powder, black salt and common salt.
3. Roll into small pills (2–3 g) and dry them in the sun.
4. When fully dry, cool and store in an airtight container. Use 2–3 balls after a meal. [Approx. **330 cal (total)**]

(iv) Indian Gooseberry Preserve

Ingredients	Quantity
Indian gooseberry	500 g
Water	2½ cups
Salt	2½–3 tsp

Method

Indian gooseberry can be preserved for about a month in brine. Put water into a container add salt, and mix. Add the gooseberries. This preserve can be used as it is with any meal. [Approx. **300 cal (total)**]

Khatta Palak Saag

Vitamins
Vitamin A: very high
Vitamin B group: low
Vitamin C: medium

Khatta palak is a very good source of iron, calcium and phosphorus. It is very beneficial in anaemia, liver ailments and asthma. It is useful in diarrhea, dysentery, piles, constipation and urinary disorders. It increases milk production in nursing mothers and helps in regulating menstrual disorders.

(i) Khatta Palak with Pulses (Dals) (5 servings)

Ingredients	Quantity
Red gram	1 cup
Water	2 cups
Khatta palak leaves (finely chopped)	100 g
Salt	to taste
Seasoning	
Ghee	1 tsp
Mustard	½ tsp
Red chilli	1
Asafoetida	a pinch
or	
Garlic flakes (crushed slightly)	6
Curry leaves	6

Method

1. Roast red gram till slightly red and cook in water in a pressure cooker.
2. Add the greens and salt and cook for a minute or two or until the dal thickens.
3. Season. The cooked preparation should be reasonably thick. [Approx. **90 cal/serving**]

Note: Red gram can be used without roasting and the amount of khatta palak can be reduced to 50 g or as required depending on the sourness required.

(ii) Khatta Palak with Onion (5 servings)

Ingredients	Quantity
Khatta palak leaves (finely chopped)	4 cups
Bengal gram (soaked, optional)	½ cup
Seasoning	
Oil	1 tbsp
Onion (finely chopped)	½ cup
Red chilli powder	½ tsp
Green chilli	1–2
Salt	to taste

Method

1. Cook khatta palak and Bengal gram in the minimum amount of water.
2. Heat oil, add onion, and fry for 3–4 minutes.
3. Add red chilli powder, green chilli, salt and the cooked vegetables. Mix and remove from fire. [Approx. 85 cal/serving]

Knol-Khol and its Leaves

Vitamins	Leaves	Knol-Khol
Vitamin A:	high	low
Vitamin B group:	high	moderate
Vitamin C:	high	moderate

Knol-khol with Dry Ginger Powder

Ingredients	Quantity
Knol-khol (thin round slices) with a few of its leaves (cut into halves or quarters)	½ kg
Water	1 cup
Salt	to taste

Ingredients	Quantity
Seasoning	
Oil	1 tsp
Green chilli	1
Asafoetida	a pinch
Dry ginger powder	1 tsp

Method

1. Heat oil and add green chillies, asafoetida, dry ginger powder, thin round slices of knol-khol and its leaves, and fry lightly for 5 minutes.
2. Add water and salt and cook till done. [Approx. 46 cal/serving]

Kundru/Kindori

Vitamins
Vitamin A: moderate
Vitamin B group: moderate
Vitamin C: low

Kundrus are very good for diabetes and are used as a diuretic. They are beneficial in cough, asthma, flatulence, edema, bile and blood ailments.

(i) Stuffed Kundru

Ingredients	Quantity
Kundru	½ kg

Method

Slit each kundru (½ kg) lengthwise for half its length, turn it around and slit again lengthwise for half its length such that the kundru still holds together. Steam cook.

Stuff with any of the following:
(a) red chilli powder (1 tsp), salt and cumin seed (½ tsp).
(b) red chilli powder (½ tsp), salt, cumin (¼ tsp), coriander seed powder (½ tsp), cumin seed powder (½ tsp) and gram flour (½ tsp—this helps to bind the slit pieces together).

(c) curry (dal) powder—see p. 94.

(d) any other stuffing as given in chapter VII (pp. 92–93. Fry these stuffed kundrus (½ kg) in a greased *kadai* or *tava* with 1 tsp oil, turning them over carefully when they are roasted on one side. They can be eaten as a snack if the stuffing is mild. [Approx. **32 cal/serving**]

(ii) Fried Kundru

Ingredients	Quantity
Kundru (1" long pieces)	½ kg
Potato (1" long pieces)	½ cup
Red chilli powder	to taste
Salt	to taste
Seasoning	
Oil	1 tsp
Onion (1" slices)	½ cup

Method

1. Steam kundru and potato.
2. Heat oil in a *kadai*, add onion and steamed vegetables.
3. Keep on fire for a few minutes till the vegetables become slightly dry.
4. Add salt, red chilli powder and fry for a minute. [Approx. **35 cal/serving**]

Lady's Fingers

Vitamins
Vitamin A: low
Vitamin B group: moderate
Vitamin C: low

Lady's Fingers is rich in sulphur, chlorine, potassium and pectose. It is very useful in urinary ailments. It is alkaline in nature and is therefore helpful in curing gastric ulcers. It is also known to be useful in dysentery, jaundice, typhoid, laryngitis, bronchitis and impotence.

Lady's Fingers with Fenugreek seed

Ingredients	Quantity
Lady's fingers (1" long pieces)	½ kg
Curd/lime juice	1 tbsp
Seasoning	
Oil	1 tsp
Fenugreek seed	½ tsp
Asafoetida	a pinch
Turmeric powder	a pinch
Salt	to taste
Red chilli powder	½ tsp
Coriander seeds powder	1 tsp
Cumin powder	½ tsp

Method

1. Add vegetable to the seasoning and cook on low fire (as given on p. 72).
2. When done, remove from fire, cool a little and add curd (1 tbsp) or lime juice. [Approx. **64 cal/serving**]

Notes: a) Wash and dry lady's fingers well before using. b) Never cook lady's fingers with water because alkaline slimy strings will be formed. However, this slime can be avoided by boiling in water to which salt, tamarind or lime juice is added even half-way through cooking. c) Cooking/frying in an open *kadai* also eliminates the slime.

Mustard Leaves

Vitamins
Vitamin A: high
Vitamin B group: low
Vitamin C: moderate

Mustard leaves strengthen heart muscles. They are useful in stomach ailments and prevent hair falling.

(i) Mustard Leaves (Saag) (10 servings)

Ingredients	Quantity
Mustard leaves (finely cut)	½ kg

Ingredients	Quantity
Spinach	¼ kg
Goosefoot white (bathua)	¼ kg
Water	½ cup
Salt	to taste
Slurry of corn or any other flour (1 tbsp) and water (½ cup)	
Tomato (finely chopped)	1 cup
Seasoning	
Oil/ghee	1 tbsp
Onion (finely chopped)	2 cups
Green chilli (finely cut/paste)	2 tsp
Ginger (grated/ground)	1 tbsp
Garlic (finely chopped)	1 tbsp

Method

1. Cook all the greens with water in a pressure cooker.
2. Add salt and mash well.
3. Add slurry and tomato and cook till the flour is cooked.
4. Season with onion, green chilli, ginger and garlic. [Approx. **52 cal/serving**]

(ii) Mustard Leaves with Garlic (3 servings)

Ingredients	Quantity
Mustard leaves (finely chopped)	¼ kg
Salt	to taste
Turmeric powder	a pinch
Seasoning	
Oil	1 tbsp
Garlic (finely chopped)	15 flakes
Green chilli	2–3

Method

1. Add garlic and green chillies to hot oil.
2. When fried, add mustard leaves, salt and turmeric powder.
3. Cook till done covering with a lid on which water is poured stir frequently. [Approx. **80 cal/serving**]

Onion Shoots (Spring Onions)

Vitamins
Vitamin A: moderate
Vitamin B group: low
Vitamin C: low

Onion Shoots with Gram Flour/Rice Flour/Whole Wheat Flour (8 servings)

Ingredients	Quantity
Onion shoots (with bulbs)	¼ kg
Garlic flakes	¼ cup
Turmeric powder	a pinch
Salt	to taste
Red chilli powder	to taste
Gram flour/rice flour/whole wheat flour/ mixed flour	½ cup
Oil	1 tbsp
Seasoning	
Oil	1 tsp
Mustard	¼ tsp
Asafoetida	a pinch

Method

1. Add onion shoots (with bulbs) and garlic flakes to the seasoning.
2. Cook in *kadai* covered with a lid.
3. When half-done add salt, mix and cook again.
4. When almost done, add flour, salt, turmeric powder and oil.
5. Mix well and keep on low fire, stirring intermittently so that the flour does not get charred.
6. When the flour is fried, add red chilli powder, mix and remove from fire. [Approx. 92 cal/serving]

Parwal

Vitamins
Vitamin A: moderate
Vitamin B group: moderate
Vitamin C: moderate

Parwal has very high medicinal and food value and is helpful in cough, blood ailments, fever, worms and aids digestion.

(i) Parwal with Cumin

Ingredients	Quantity
Parwal (1 cm cubes)	½ kg
Water	1 cup
Seasoning	
Oil	1 tsp
Cumin	½ tsp
Asafoetida	a pinch
Turmeric powder	¼ tsp
Red chilli powder	½ tsp
Coriander seed powder	½ tsp

Method

1. Boil parwal in water.
2. Add seasoning and salt. [Approx. **25 cal/serving**]

(ii) Stuffed Parwal (3 servings)

Ingredients		Quantity
Parwal		¼ kg
Stuffing		
Cumin powder	⎫	½ tsp
Red chilli powder	⎬ mix	¼ tsp
Thick tamarind extract/		¼ tsp
raw mango powder	⎭	
Salt		to taste
Oil		1 tsp

Method

1. Slit the parwal into quarters, without cutting the base.
2. Fill with stuffing.
3. Heat oil in a non-stick pan or *kadai*, add parwal, and cover *kadai* with a lid on which water is poured.
4. Cook on low fire till done, sprinkling a little water on the parwal as and when needed but without stirring it too often. [Approx. **38 cal/serving**]

Note: An alternative method of cooking stuffed parwal is to slit the parwal, steam it and then stuff it. Fry in a frying pan or on a *tava* with 1 tsp oil.

(iii) Parwal peel and seed Chutney/Dosas

See vegetable peel chutney on p. 244.

Potato

> *Vitamins*
> Vitamin A: low
> Vitamin B group: high
> Vitamin C: low

Potato boiled with its skin is not hard to digest. It only becomes heavy when fried or eaten with other oily and rich food. In fact potato (starch) is as good as (if not better than) rice. Potato starch is said to prevent the fermentation of other food in the stomach. It is a good source of minerals like potassium, magnesium, iron, phosphorus and copper. It is highly alkaline. Potatoes should be eaten baked (whole) for maximum food value and should be boiled with their skin for minimum loss of nutrients as some of these nutrients lie below the skin. An excessive intake of potatoes is harmful for those who are obese or diabetic. Potato is rich in carbohydrates. The juice of raw potatoes is beneficial in gout and rheumatism as it dissolves uric acid and in the treatment of ulcers. Raw potato juice is excellent for skin blemishes, as a poultice for swellings and conjunctivitis, for stomach and intestinal disorders. Some potatoes may have green patches; these bits should not be eaten as they contain a harmful chemical, solanine.

(i) Grated Potato Curry (high calorie)

Ingredients	Quantity
Potato (grated)	½ kg
Roasted groundnuts with skin (powdered)	2 tbsp
Salt	to taste
Jaggery (bits or powder)	½ tsp

Ingredients	Quantity
Seasoning	
Oil or ghee	4 tbsp
Green chilli	2–3
Cumin	½ tsp

Method

1. Add green chillies, cumin, and potato to hot ghee or oil and cover pan. Stir intermittently.
2. When half-cooked, add groundnut powder, salt and jaggery. Cook till done. [Approx. **201 cal/serving**]

(ii) Potato Gravy Curry with Onion and Tomato (3 servings)

Ingredients	Quantity
Potato (1" cubes) (cooked)	¼ kg
Tomato (cut into quarters)	½ cup
Turmeric powder	a pinch
Salt	to taste
Coriander seed powder	1 tsp
Water	2¼ cups
Seasoning	
Ghee or oil	1 tsp
Onion (finely chopped)	½ cup

Method

1. Heat oil and add onion, tomato, turmeric powder, salt and coriander seed powder. Fry for a minute or two.
2. Add ¼ cup water and cook till tomato softens.
3. Add cooked potatoes and 2 cups water and boil. [Approx. **112 cal/ serving**]

(iii) Potato with Bengal Gram flour

Ingredients	Quantity
Bengal gram flour	2 tbsp
Water	3–4 cups
Thick tamarind extract	2 tbsp

Method

To an upma-type seasoned vegetable (see p. 79) add slurry and thick tamarind extract, and boil till the flour is cooked. [Approx. **120 cal/serving**]

(iv) Potato with Onion, Tomato and Poppy Seed (Khus Khus) Gravy

Ingredients		Quantity
Potato (1" cubes)		½ kg
Tomato (cut into quarter)		1 cup
Turmeric powder		a pinch
Green chilli		1
Salt		to taste
Poppy seed	grind	1 tbsp
Cloves	finely	6–7
Garlic		1–2 flakes
Ginger		½" piece
Fried onion (finely chopped)		½ cup
Oil		1 tsp

Method

1. Boil and peel potato and cut into cubes.
2. Heat oil in a pan and add potato, tomato and the paste.
3. Mix and keep on fire for a minute.
4. Add water and cook till tomato softens a little. [Approx. **114 cal/serving**]

Ridge Gourd

Vitamins
Vitamin A: low
Vitamin B group: low
Vitamin C: high

(i) Ridge Gourd with Poppy Seed

Ingredients	Quantity
Ridge gourd (small pieces)	½ kg
Water	½ cup
Poppy seed (powder/paste)	1 tbsp

Ingredients	Quantity
Green chilli (pieces/paste)	½ tsp
Garlic (crushed/pieces)	2–3 flakes
Fresh coconut (grated) (optional) .	2 tbsp

Method

1. Cook the gourd in water.
2. Add powder or paste of poppy seed, green chilli and fried garlic.
3. Fresh grated coconut may also be added as garnishing or ground with the other ingredients. [Approx. **36 cal/serving**]

(ii) Ridge Gourd Chutney

See Ridge gourd or Smooth gourd chutney on p. 242. Also see vegetable peel chutney on p. 244.

(iii) Ridge Gourd Dosas

See pp. 196, 198 and 199.

(iv) Traditional Andhra Dish with Curry Powder

See Brinjal on p. 114. Peel ridge gourd, cut gourd into 1" long pieces (½ kg) and use this for curry.

Make chutney/dosas with the ridge gourd peel as given above in (ii) and (iii).

(v) Ridge Gourd Peel Curry

Ingredients	Quantity
Ridge gourd	½ kg
Water	1 tbsp
Oil	1 tsp
Red chilli powder	to taste
Salt	to taste
Fresh coconut (grated)/roasted sesame seed	1 tbsp
Roasted groundnuts with skin (powdered)	1 tbsp
Coriander leaves (finely chopped)	1 tbsp
Seasoning	
Oil	½ tsp

Ingredients	Quantity
Mustard	½ tsp
Cumin	¼ tsp
Asafoetida	a pinch
Curry leaves	6–8
Onion (finely chopped)	½–1 cup

Method

1. Peel ridge gourd and chop the peel finely.
2. Cook with minimum water or oil on low fire in a *kadai* covered with a lid on which water is poured.
3. When cooked, season with mustard, cumin, asafoetida, curry leaves and onion.
4. Add red chilli powder and salt to taste, and add coconut and/or roasted sesame seed, groundnut powder and coriander leaves. Mix well. [Approx. **49 cal/serving**]

Note: The chopped peel may also be pressure cooked or steamed. Drain (or evaporate) any remaining water and then proceed as above.

Radish

Vitamins	Radish	Its Leaves
Vitamin A:	low	very high
Vitamin B group:	moderate	high
Vitamin C:	low	moderate

Radish contains a volatile, sulphurated oil. Radish should be eaten raw as the vitamin C is destroyed during cooking. The juice of tender radish leaves is useful in jaundice as well as in piles. It is a digestive tonic, increases appetite and improves digestion. It is very useful for anaemia, rheumatism, tuberculosis, scurvy, heart diseases and respiratory diseases. Radish leaves are a good laxative.

(i) Radish with Pulses

Ingredients	Quantity
Radish (grated)	½ kg

Ingredients	Quantity
Split Bengal gram or green gram (cooked/soaked)	¼ to ½ cup
Salt	to taste
Water	2 tbsp
Fresh coconut (grated)	1 tbsp
Coriander leaves (finely chopped)	1 tbsp
Seasoning	
Oil	1 tsp
Mustard	1 tsp
Asafoetida	a pinch
Garlic (coarsely pounded)	6–8 flakes
Green chilli paste	½ tsp
Cumin	½ tsp
Curry leaves	6–8

Method

1. Add the radish and Bengal gram (preferably green gram) to the seasoning.
2. Cook on low fire adding water and salt and mix.
3. Garnish with coconut and coriander leaves. [Approx. **56** cal/serving]

Note: Radish and pulses can be steamed together and then seasoned.

(ii) Radish with Tomato

Ingredients	Quantity
Oil	1 tsp
Onion (1" long pieces)	1 cup
Radish (grated) and its leaves (finely chopped)	½ kg
Tomato (cut into quarters)	1 cup
Salt	to taste
Seasoning	
Black gram	1 tsp
Asafoetida	a pinch
Mustard	½ tsp
Green chilli (paste)	½ tsp
Curry leaves	6–8

Ingredients	Quantity
Coriander leaves (finely chopped)	1–2 tbsp
Fresh coconut (grated)	2 tbsp

Method

1. To hot oil add onion, fry a little and add radish and its leaves.
2. Add tomato and cook till done.
3. Add salt and season with black gram, asafoetida, mustard, green chilli and curry leaves.
4. Garnish with coriander leaves and coconut, both optional. [Approx. **55 cal/serving**]

Note: In this recipe, the pungent odour of radish is minimised.

(iii) *Radish with all raw ingredients*

Ingredients		Quantity
Radish (finely diced/coarsely grated)		½ kg
Water		2 cups
Tomato (finely chopped)		1 cup
Coriander leaves (finely chopped)		½ cup
Green chilli	ground to	1
Onion (finely chopped)	a paste	½ cup
Cumin		¼ tsp
Turmeric powder		a pinch
Salt		to taste

Method

1. Cook radish in water.
2. Add paste and salt and remove from fire. [Approx. **25 cal/serving**]

Raw Banana

Vitamins
Vitamin A: low
Vitamin B group: low
Vitamin C: low

(i) Fried Raw Banana

See pp. 72, 73. [Approx. 408 cal (total)]

(ii) Raw Banana Upma Sabji

See p. 73. [Approx. 492 cal (total)]

(iii) Sweet and Sour Raw Banana (Pulusu Pettina Kura)

See p. 78. [Approx. 354 cal (total)]

(iv) Raw Banana with simple seasoning

See pp. 74–75. [Approx. 402 cal (total)]

(v) Raw Banana Sour Gravy with Steamed Vegetable (Pulusu Pachadi)

See p. 112 (v). [Approx. 540 cal (total)]

(vi) Raw Banana Cutlets

Raw banana cutlets are made in the same way as potato cutlets.

Raw Jack Fruit

Vitamins
Vitamin A:
Vitamin B group: low
Vitamin C: low

(i) Raw Jackfruit with Pulses

Ingredients	Quantity
Raw jackfruit	½ kg
Water	½ cup
Salt	to taste
Red gram (pre-cooked)	¼ cup
Bengal gram (pre-soaked)	¼ cup
Fresh coconut (grated)	¼ cup
Seasoning	
Oil	1 tsp
Black gram	1 tsp

Ingredients	Quantity
Mustard	½ tsp
Asafoetida	a pinch
Curry leaves	6–8
Onion (small pieces)	½ cup
Green chilli (paste)/powder	1 tsp
Red chilli	1 or 2

Method

1. Pressure cook cleaned and diced jackfruit in water.
2. Add salt and cooked red gram and/or cooked Bengal gram and coconut.
3. Add seasoning. [Approx. **92 cal/serving**]

Note: The cooked jackfruit should be coarsely mashed to make it taste better. Fried papad and fryums go well with it.

(ii) Raw Jackfruit with Gravy

Ingredients		Quantity
Jackfruit		½ kg
Water		2 cups
Garlic		6–8 flakes
Ginger	roasted and	½" piece
Green chilli	ground to	2
Sesame seed	a paste	1 tbsp
Fresh coconut (grated)		1 tbsp
Seasoning		
Black gram		1 tsp
Mustard		½ tsp
Green chilli		1 or 2
Curry leaves		6–8

Method

1. Boil cleaned and diced jackfruit in water and add the paste.
2. Season with black gram, mustard, green chilli and curry leaves.
3. Mix and mash coarsely; add salt. [Approx. **82 cal/serving**]

Raw Papaya

Vitamins
Vitamin A:
Vitamin B group: low
Vitamin C: low

Raw papaya is a good liver tonic. It is very useful in digestive disorders, cough, acidity, heart ailments, eliminating intestinal worms etc. It stimulates milk secretion in lactating mothers. Its milk is very useful in skin diseases. Rubbing the white pulp of raw papaya on pimples is beneficial. Cook till just done on low fire to make it tasty and to preserve its enzymes.

(i) Raw Papaya with Thick Gravy

Ingredients		Quantity
Raw papaya		½ kg
Turmeric powder		a pinch
Green gram (with skin, presoaked)		½ cup
Water		2 cups
Salt		to taste
Coriander seed		1 tbsp
Bengal gram (paste)		1 tbsp
Black gram		1 tbsp
Mustard		1 tsp
Red chilli	roasted and ground to a paste	2–3
Cumin		1 tsp
Garlic		3–4
Onion (finely sliced)		½ cup
Fresh coconut (grated)		2–3 tbsp
Seasoning		
Black gram		1 tsp
Mustard		½ tsp
Red chilli		1
Asafoetida		a pinch
Curry leaves		6–8

Method

1. Cook the cleaned and finely diced/coarsely grated papaya with turmeric powder, and green gram in water.
2. Add salt and the paste.

3. Boil for five minutes and add seasoning. [Approx. **100 cal/serving**]

(ii) Raw Papaya with Simple Seasoning

Ingredients	Quantity
Raw papaya	½ kg
Water	1 tbsp
Lime juice	1 tbsp
Fresh coconut (grated)	2 tbsp
Coriander leaves (finely chopped)	2 tbsp
Seasoning	
Oil	1 tsp
Bengal gram	1 tsp
Black gram	1 tsp
Mustard	½ tsp
Asafoetida	a pinch
Green chillies	2
Red chilli	1
Curry leaves	3–6
Salt	to taste
Turmeric powder	a pinch

Method

1. Cook coarsely grated papaya in water on low fire.
2. Add seasoning.
3. Keep on fire for a minute and remove. Add lime juice, grated coconut and coriander leaves and mix well. [Approx. **91 cal/serving**]

(iii) Raw Papaya Chutney (5 servings)

Ingredients	Quantity
Raw papaya	¼ kg
Water	1 tbsp
Seasoning	
Oil	1 tsp
Black gram	2 tsp
Fenugreek seed	¼ tsp
Mustard	½ tsp

Ingredients	Quantity
Asafoetida	a pinch
Green/red chilli	2 to 3
Turmeric powder	a pinch

Method

1. Cook finely-diced papaya on low heat without adding water.
2. Roast the ingredients of the seasoning in oil.
3. Pound these coarsely with salt and tamarind (or lime juice).
4. Add the cooked papaya, and mash or grind coarsely.
5. Raw onion or fresh coriander leaves may also be added while grinding the seasoning. [Approx. **35 cal/serving**]

Pumpkin

Vitamins
Vitamin A: high
Vitamin B group: moderate
Vitamin C: low

Red pumpkin can be eaten instead of chapatis in the case of diabetes and obesity. It is useful in tuberculosis and haemorrhoids. It removes worms, cures acidity and is a diuretic.

(i) Pumpkin with Sweet and Sour Gravy (Pachipulusu Pachadi)

Ingredients	Quantity
Pumpkin (1" cubes)	½ kg
Water	1 cup
Salt	to taste
Tomato (ripe) (1" cubes)	½ to 1 cup
Turmeric powder	a pinch
Coriander leaves (finely chopped)	1 tbsp
Seasoning	
Black gram	½ tsp
Mustard	¼ tsp
Cumin	¼ tsp
Asafoetida	a pinch
Curry leaves	6–8
Onion (finely chopped)	½ cup
Red or green chilli (paste/pieces)	to taste

Method

1. Boil/steam pumpkin in water.
2. Add salt, ripe tomato, turmeric powder and coriander leaves.
3. Add seasoning.
4. Mash by hand (removing the red or green chillies while mashing), adding as much water as is required.
5. Tomato may be replaced by tamarind. A little jaggery may also be added. [Approx. 42 **cal/serving**]

(ii) Pumpkin and Cluster Beans with Thyme

Ingredients	Quantity
Cluster beans (1" long pieces)	1 cup
Pumpkin (1 inch cubes)	½ kg
Turmeric powder	a pinch
Salt	to taste
Seasoning	
Oil	1 tsp
Thyme	½–1 tsp
Red chilli	1
Curry leaves	6–8

Method

1. Steam cluster beans and pumpkin without water.
2. To the seasoning, add cluster beans and pumpkin and turmeric powder.
3. Keep on low fire for a minute, add salt and mix well. [Approx. 32 **cal/serving**]

(iii) Pumpkin Peel Curry

See Ridge gourd peel curry in this chapter.

Smooth Gourd

Vitamins
Vitamin A: moderate
Vitamin B group: low
Vitamin C:

(i) Smooth Gourd with Curry Powder (3 servings)

See p. 76.

Just one potato cooked along with the gourd gives it a smooth consistency, improves the taste and absorbs the excess water. In addition, a little whole wheat flour sprinkled on top also absorbs water. Brinjal combines well with smooth gourd. [Approx. 42 cal/serving]

(ii) Smooth Gourd Bajjis on Tava

See Bajjis on *tava* on p. 219. [Approx. 1150 cal (total)]

(iii) Smooth Gourd with Garlic Paste

Ingredients	Quantity
Smooth gourd (1 cm round pieces)	$\frac{1}{2}$ kg
Seasoning	
Oil	1 tsp.
Black gram	1 tsp
Mustard	$\frac{1}{4}$ tsp
Curry leaves	6–8
Green chilli paste	$\frac{1}{2}$ tsp
Ginger–garlic paste	$\frac{1}{2}$–1 tsp

Method

1. Cook the gourd in minimum water.
2. Add salt and seasoning and mix well. [Approx. **32 cal/serving**]

Snake Gourd

Vitamins
Vitamin A: low
Vitamin B group: low
Vitamin C:

Snake gourd is nutritive and has a cooling effect on the body. It is helpful in diabetes, obesity and tuberculosis. It is also a cardiac tonic and counteracts fever.

(i) Stuffed Snake Gourd

See recipes for Stuffed Vegetables on pp. 92–99. [Approx. 52 cal/serving]

(ii) Snake Gourd Raita

See Boiled Vegetable Raita on p. 247. [Approx. 67 cal/serving]

(iii) Snake Gourd Kootu

See p. 56–57. [Approx. 46 cal/serving]

String Beans (Slender Beans)

Vitamins
Vitamin A: low
Vitamin B group: moderate
Vitamin C: moderate

This vegetable contains silica and has insulin-like properties, so it is helpful for diabetics.

(i) String Beans with Potato

See p. 72. [Approx. 75 cal/serving]
See p. 73. [Approx. 100 cal/serving]

(ii) String Beans with Simple Seasoning and Coconut

See p. 75.

Spinach

Vitamins
Vitamin A: high
Vitamin B group: moderate
Vitamin C: moderate

Spinach is a very good source of protein and iron. It is a very important food during pregnancy and lactation. It prevents abortions. It is a good source of calcium, is alkaline in nature and thus helps in neutralising acidity. Its leaves are very good for dental health, and prevent and cure night blindness. Spinach is a diuretic, a mild laxative and is an excellent remedy for constipation nourishing the intestines and toning up their movement. Infusion of spinach with fenugreek seed and honey helps in bronchitis, tuberculosis and asthma. Spinach is very effective in the treatment of anaemia due to its high iron content.

(i) Spinach–Dal–Potato Gravy (8 servings)

Ingredients	Quantity
Spinach	½ kg
or spinach plus beetroot leaves	¼ kg each
Bengal gram (split)	3 tbsp
Potato (½" cubes)	½ cup
Tomato (½" cubes)	1 cup
or tamarind	1 lime-size ball
Ginger (finely chopped)	1 tsp
Onion (finely chopped)	1 cup
Water	2 cups
Salt	to taste
Seasoning	
Oil	1 tsp
Garlic (finely chopped)	6–8 flakes
Onion (finely chopped)	½ cup

Method

1. Pressure cook (altogether), split Bengal gram, potato, tomato or tamarind, ginger, onion and greens in water till done.
2. Season with garlic and onion. [Approx. **62 cal/serving**]

(ii) Spinach–Pulses Gravy (8 servings)

Ingredients	Quantity
Spinach (finely chopped)	½ kg
or	
Spinach and beetroot leaves	¼ kg each
Green gram (with skin)	½ cup
Bottle gourd (½" pieces)	¼ kg
Water	3 cups

Ingredients	Quantity
Salt	to taste
Ginger (paste/chopped)	$\frac{1}{2}$ tsp
Seasoning	
Oil	1 tsp
Black gram	$\frac{1}{2}$ tsp
Mustard	$\frac{1}{2}$ tsp
Cumin	$\frac{1}{4}$ tsp
Green chilli paste	$\frac{1}{4}$ tsp

Method

1. Pressure cook the green gram and bottle gourd in water.
2. Add the greens. Cook till done and add salt.*
3. Add seasoning and then ginger paste.
4. Mix and remove from fire. [Approx. 55 cal/serving]

Sweet Potato

Vitamins
Vitamin A: low
Vitamin B group: moderate
Vitamin C: low

(i) Sweet Potato Pulusu (4 servings)

Ingredients	Quantity
Sweet potato (1" thick slices)	$\frac{1}{4}$ kg
Water	2 cups
Thick tamarind extract	2 tsp
Salt	to taste
Turmeric powder	a pinch
Jaggery	1 lime-sized ball
Green chilli	1
Slurry of rice or whole wheat flour (1 tbsp) with water ($\frac{1}{2}$ cup)	

---

*If sour gravy is desired, thick tamarind extract (1 lime-sized ball of tamarind), jaggery (1 lime-sized ball) and a slurry of rice or whole wheat flour (1 tsp in 2 tbsp water) can be added to thicken the gravy. Keep on fire for a minute or two till the flour is cooked.

Ingredients	Quantity
Seasoning	
Oil	1 tsp
Black gram (optional)	1 tsp
Mustard	½ tsp
Red chilli	1 or 2
Asafoetida	a pinch
Curry leaves	6–8

Method

1. Cook sweet potato in water.
2. Add tamarind, salt, turmeric powder, jaggery, green chilli, whole wheat flour slurry and boil for a minute or two till the flour is cooked.
3. Add water to get the desired consistency.
4. Season. [Approx. **140 cal/serving**]

Note: The gravy has a tendency to thicken when cold. More water should then be added to get a thinner consistency. Alternatively, instead of adding a slurry of flour, mash the cooked dish slightly to achieve the required thickness of gravy.

(ii) Sweet Potato Chutney

See p. 243. [Approx. **225 cal (total)**]

Tinda

Vitamins
Vitamin A: low
Vitamin B group: low
Vitamin C: low

(i) Tinda with Coconut and Tamarind Paste

Ingredients	Quantity
Tinda (1 cm cubes)	½ kg
Water	½ cup
Fresh coconut (grated)	1 tbsp
Tamarind or raw mango	to taste
Salt	to taste

Ingredients	Quantity
Red chilli powder	½ tsp
Turmeric powder	a pinch

Method

1. Steam Tinda in water.
2. Evaporate the water and add the paste of coconut, tamarind or raw mango, salt, red chilli powder and turmeric powder.
3. Keep on fire for a minute or two. [Approx. **38 cal/serving**]

(ii) Tinda with Garlic Paste

Ingredients	Quantity
Tinda (I cm cubes)	½ kg
Water	2 tbsps
Salt	to taste
Fresh coconut (grated)	2 tsp
Ginger (pounded)	¼ tsp
Cumin–coriander seeds powder	1 tsp
Seasoning	
Oil	1 tsp
Black gram	1 tsp
Mustard	½ tsp
Green chilli	1
Curry leaves	4–6
Onion (finely chopped)	¼ cup
Garlic (crushed)	2–4 flakes

Method

Cook tinda in water and add the seasoning, salt, coconut, ginger, cumin–coriander seed powder and mix well. [Approx. 45 cal/serving]

(iii) Tinda with Sesame, Groundnut and Poppy Seed

Ingredients	Quantity
Tinda (I cm cubes)	½ kg
Water	½ cup
Fresh coconut (grated)	1 tbsp
Roasted sesame seeds	1 tsp
Roasted groundnuts with skin	6

Ingredients	Quantity
Roasted poppy seed	1 tsp
Green chilli	1
Seasoning	
Oil	½ tsp
Mustard	¼ tsp
Red chillies	2
Curry leaves	4–6

Method

1. Cook tinda in water, evaporate the leftover water and add seasoning.
2. Grind to a paste fresh coconut grated, roasted sesame seeds, roasted ground nut with skin, roasted poppy seed and green chilli.
3. Add the paste. [Approx. **53 cal/serving**]

(iv) Tinda Peel Chutney/Dosas

See Vegetable Peel Chutney on p. 244.

Tomato

Vitamins
Vitamin A: moderate
Vitamin B group: moderate
Vitamin C: moderate

Tomatoes are moderately rich in vitamins A, B, C and minerals (calcium, iron, potassium) and are therefore alkaline. Their acid taste is due to the citric acid they contain. They also have oxalic acid. They are good for indigestion and liver problems. The vitamin C content in tomato is not quickly destroyed because it is protected by the acid.

(i) Tomato with Coconut and Onion (2 servings)

Ingredients	Quantity
Fresh coconut (grated)	1 cup
Onion	1 cup
Tomato	1 cup

Ingredients	Quantity
Green chilli	1 or 2
Garlic	8–10 flakes
Curry leaves	12–18
Salt	to taste

Method

1. Mix all the ingredients and cook on low fire till done without adding water. [Approx. **66 cal/serving**]

(ii) Tomato with Fried Onion and Coconut Paste (4 servings)

Ingredients	Quantity
Tomato (finely diced)	2 cups
Paste of fresh coconut	2 tbsp
Water	½ cup
Jaggery (optional)	to taste
Salt	to taste
Seasoning	
Oil	1 tsp
Mustard	1 tsp
Red chilli	1
Cumin	½ tsp
Onion (finely chopped)	1 cup
Green chilli	1

Method

1. Add tomatoes to the seasoning and cook on low fire.
2. When almost done, add the coconut paste, salt and water and cook till done.
3. Add jaggery (optional). [Approx. **62 cal/serving**]

(iii) Tomato Rasam

(a) With Green Coriander and Curry Leaves (5 servings)

Ingredients	Quantity
Ripe tomato (cut into quarters)	5 medium-size
Green coriander (finely chopped)	2 tbsp
Curry leaves (finely chopped)	2 tsp
Asafoetida	a pinch

Ingredients	Quantity
Rasam/sambar powder	2 tsp
Salt	to taste
Red gram (pre-cooked)	½ cup
Seasoning	
Ghee	½ tsp
Cumin	¼ tsp
Mustard	¼ tsp

Method

1. Put tomato, coriander, curry leaves, asafoetida, sambar/rasam powder and salt into water and mix thoroughly, mashing the tomato a little.
2. Boil till cooked, add pre-cooked red gram and mix. Season and serve hot. [Approx. **51 cal/serving**]

Note: This mild rasam may also be served as an appetiser.

(b) With Tomato and Tamarind (4 servings)

Ingredients	Quantity
Ripe tomato (cut into quarters)	¼ kg
Thick tamarind extract or juice of one lime	1 tbsp
Red gram (boiled)	1 tbsp
Water	2–3 cups
Ginger–green chilli (paste/pieces)	1 tsp each
Seasoning	
Oil	1 tsp
Mustard	½ tsp
Fenugreek seed	¼ tsp
Asafoetida	a pinch
Cumin	¼ tsp
Salt	to taste
Turmeric powder	a pinch
Coriander leaves (finely chopped)	1 tbsp

Method

1. Pressure cook tomato in 1 tbsp water.
2. Strain, add thick tamarind extract or lime juice, boiled red gram, water, ginger–green chilli pieces/paste.

3. Add the seasoning. Boil once and garnish with coriander leaves. [Approx. **55 cal/serving**]

(iv) Tomato Dal

See p. 57 (iii).

Turnip

Vitamins	Turnip	Turnip Leaves
Vitamin A:	—	high
Vitamin B group:	moderate	high
Vitamin C:	moderate	high

Turnips are helpful in anaemia, high blood pressure, liver ailments and dental health. They are good blood purifiers.

(i) Turnip with Tomato

Ingredients	Quantity
Turnip (1 cm cubes)	½ kg
Tomato (finely diced)	1 cup
Water	1 tbsp
Seasoning	
Oil	1 tsp
Cumin	½ tsp
Asafoetida	a pinch
Red chilli powder	½ tsp
Salt	to taste

Method

1. Cook turnip with tomato and water in a pressure cooker.
2. Mash the boiled vegetables.
3. Add seasoning and mix well. [Approx. **42 cal/serving**]

(ii) Turnip with Spinach

Ingredients	Quantity
Turnip (1 cm cubes)	½ kg
Spinach (finely chopped)	200 g
Bengal gram	1 tbsp

Ingredients	Quantity
Water	½ cup
Seasoning	
Oil	1 tsp
Onion (finely chopped)	1 cup
Garlic	6–8 flakes
Ginger (finely chopped)	1" piece
Green chilli	1–2

Method

1. Cook turnip, spinach and Bengal gram in ½ cup water in a pressure cooker.
2. Add seasoning and salt, and mix well. [Approx. **60 cal/ serving**]

Yam

Vitamins
Vitamin A: moderate
Vitamin B group: moderate
Vitamin C:

Cooked yam with curd is useful in dysentery, diarrhoea and piles. It causes acidity when taken too frequently.

(i) Yam Sambar without pulses (5 servings)

Ingredients	Quantity
Yam (pre-boiled and coarsely mashed)	½ cup
Vegetables like bottle gourd, brinjal, chow-chow marrow, onion, beans, cauliflower, cabbage etc. (½–1" pieces)	½ kg (total)
Water	4 cups
Thick tamarind extract	2 tbsp
Salt	to taste
Turmeric powder	¼ tsp
Green chilli	2
Jaggery	½ tsp
Curry leaves	4–6
Sambar powder	2–3 tsp
Fresh coconut (grated)	1 tbsp

Ingredients	Quantity
Coriander leaves (finely chopped)	2 tbsp
Seasoning	
Oil	1 tsp
Mustard	½ tsp
Onion (finely chopped)	¼ cup
Asafoetida	a pinch
Curry leaves	6–8

Method

1. Boil all the vegetables in 2 cups water.
2. Add mashed yam, tamarind extract, salt, turmeric powder, green chilli, jaggery, curry leaves, sambar powder, and 2 cups water and cook till done.
3. Add grated coconut, and seasoning.
4. Boil for a minute and garnish with coriander leaves. [Approx. **68 cal/serving**]

(ii) Yam Pulusu (5 servings)

Ingredients	Quantity
Mustard	½ tsp
Fenugreek seed	¼ tsp
Asafoetida	a pinch
Red chilli	1

Method

1. Instead of sambar powder, add above powder.
2. The rest of the procedure is the same as in **Recipe (i)**. [Approx. **65 cal/serving**]

SPICES, HERBS AND GARNISHINGS

Onion

Vitamins
Vitamin A: —
Vitamin B group: low
Vitamin C: low

Onion has great therapeutic value. It contains volatile sulphur compounds like methyl disulphide. (This is what makes it pungent.) It is used as a diuretic, stimulant and expectorant. It is an excellent antidote for bee and wasp stings. It liquefies phlegm and prevents further formation. It is very useful in cough, cold, influenza and bronchitis. It is curative as well as preventive. It is a good source of sulphur and potassium along with calcium, iron, sodium and phosphorus.

Onion has strong antibiotic, antibacterial and antitoxic properties. It is good for asthma, tuberculoses, insomnia, anaemia, nervous disorders, blood circulation, piles, skin diseases, cholera, sexual debility, heart diseases and menstrual disorders. The white variety is superior to the red one. Raw onion has more nutritive and medicinal value than cooked onion.

Garlic

Vitamins
Vitamin A: —
Vitamin B group: moderate
Vitamin C: low

Garlic has been used as a medicine since ancient times for bronchitis, asthma, tuberculoses, fever, deafness, leprosy, worms, liver and spleen ailments, heart diseases, arteriosclerosis etc. It contains minerals like sulphur, iodine and chlorine in addition to calcium, iron and phosphorus. It contains a very powerful antiseptic. Garlic purifies blood, stimulates blood-circulation, regulates the digestive system, prevents heart attacks, cures skin infections and is a revitalizer. It is regarded as the most effective remedy for lowering blood pressure and blood cholesterol, gout and rheumatism, elimination of worms, whooping cough and diphtheria. It is a good tonic for loss of sexual power, sexual debility and impotence. Recently it has also been used successfully in managing cancer.

Ginger

Vitamins
Vitamin A: low
Vitamin B group: moderate
Vitamin C: low

Ginger has been used in India since the Vedic period and is available in two forms: fresh and dried. Both possess curative properties. Ginger is very good for digestive disorders and acts as an anti-flatulent. Finely chopped ginger mixed with lime juice turns red after a few hours and is used as a digestive medicine. Dry ginger with jaggery helps in jaundice and kills worms. Ginger is an excellent remedy for respiratory ailments. Fresh ginger juice with honey cures a cough and cold when taken 3–4 times a day. Ginger tea is very effective in bronchitis, asthma, whooping cough and tuberculosis of the lungs. It can cure all types of pain including headache, earache, toothache and pain in joints. Ginger is also very helpful in amenorrhoea (absence of menses), dymenorrhea (painful menses) and poor semen production.

Coriander Leaves

Vitamins
Vitamin A: very high
Vitamin B group: high
Vitamin C: high

Coriander is a good source of vitamins A, B, C and iron. It is useful in tuberculosis, asthma, allergies, heart diseases, anaemia and indigestion. The juice of fresh coriander leaves is helpful in vomiting, whooping cough, jaundice, piles, dysentery, typhoid, migraine and gastric ulcers.

Curry Leaves

Vitamins
Vitamin A: very high
Vitamin B group: high
Vitamin C: low

Curry leaves are a good herbal tonic and a good source of vitamins A and B. They are helpful in nausea and indigestion caused by eating fatty food. They are also beneficial for children who are teething and for those with pimples. Fresh curry leaves with honey are useful in piles, dysentery, diarrhoea and diabetes.

Mint

Vitamins
Vitamin A: high
Vitamin B group: high
Vitamin C: moderate

Mint is a good source of vitamins A, B, C, D, E and minerals like calcium, phosphorus, iron and sulphur. It is an appetizer and helps the digestive process, liver ailments and nausea/vomiting. It is anti-bacterial, and is effective in controlling palpitation, menstrual irregularities, asthma and fever.

Lime

Vitamins
Vitamin A: low
Vitamin B group: low
Vitamin C: high

Lime is a very good source of vitamin C and has been used as a medicine in India from ancient times. The vitamin C content of lime increases the resistance of the body against diseases, and is good for teeth and bones too. It cleanses the body, breaks up mucous and yields an alkaline end-product. It is helpful in the healing of wounds and in the treatment of digestive disorders, indigestion, vomiting, acidity, peptic ulcers, constipation, tonsilitis, joint pains, bleeding piles, obesity and inflammation of the bladder. Lime juice should be diluted with lukewarm water.

Mango (Raw)

Vitamins
Vitamin A: low

Vitamin B group: low
Vitamin C: moderate

Raw Mango is used as a treatment for summer diarrhea, piles, morning sickness, indigestion and constipation. It is good for the liver, formation of blood and scurvy.

Coconut

Vitamins
Vitamin A: —
Vitamin B group: moderate
Vitamin C: low

Fresh coconut is a highly nutritious and fattening fruit. It is a rich source of fibre and high quality protein, potassium, sodium, magnesium and sulphur. It is beneficial in the treatment of digestive disorders, acidity, intestinal worms, vomiting, cough, urinary disorders and skin ailments.

Groundnut

Vitamins
Vitamin A: low
Vitamin B group: high
Vitamin C: —

This is a highly nutritious food, rich in protein, phosphorus, thiamine and niacin. It is very good for growing children, pregnant women and nursing mothers. It builds resistance against infection. Groundnut is useful for women with heavy bleeding during menstruation, and in obesity and diabetes.

Salt

Normally the quantity of salt that a person needs it is said is less than half a gram per day; this is provided even by raw vegetables. An excessive intake of salt is excreted through the kidneys which can eliminate 4–5 g of salt daily. The excess salt deposited in the body causes heart diseases, high blood pressure, arthritis, obesity

and even cancer. The salt from fruits and vegetables is termed
organic salt. The salt used as an additive is inorganic salt (a
chemical). Organic salt is easily assimilated by the body, and helps
in digestion, strengthens bones and is also required for the
elimination of carbon dioxide from the system. A deficiency of this
organic salt results in respiratory diseases. Inorganic salt cannot
carry out all these functions in the body. Black salt or rock salt can
be a good substitute for this purpose.

Coriander Seed

This seed is beneficial in blood dysentery, nausea and diarrhoea,
insomnia and headache. It is also beneficial to the eyes as well as
being effective in anaemia.

Pepper

Pepper is a good worm-expeller. It helps in cough, dysentery and
skin diseases, relieves flatulence and is a nerve tonic.

Thyme

Thyme is an antiseptic. It helps relieve joint pain, stomach pain
and chest pain. It is a good remedy for menstrual disorders, gives
relief from lumbago and helps in cleansing the uterus. It cures
indigestion, loss of appetite, constipation and flatulence. It is also
a nerve tonic.

Turmeric Powder

This powder is antiseptic and is routinely used in Indian cooking.
It helps in relieving flatulence and cough, heals wounds and is a
pain reliever. It is said to have an anti-tetanus effect and is also
anti-cancerous.

Mustard Seed

Mustard seed is used as an analgesic in rheumatism, sciatica and to
combat the ill-effects of poisoning and narcotics and in other kinds
of muscle pain.

Clove

Clove has valuable medicinal properties. It is considered beneficial in headache, toothache, whooping cough and vomiting. It is also helpful in acidity, stys, cholera and measles.

Fenugreek Seed

Fenugreek seed is diuretic and helps in indigestion. It increases milk secretion in nursing mothers. It is a soothing agent and acts as a cleanser. A paste made of fenugreek seed applied on the scalp helps get rid of dandruff. Tea made from fenugreek seed brings down fevers, cleanses the stomach, heals peptic ulcers and respiratory diseases. Fenugreek seed is most effective in diabetes and joint pain.

Asafoetida

This is very good for digestion and increases appetite. A paste of asafoetida mixed in water relieves colic when applied over the stomach, and headache when applied on the forehead. It is helpful in low blood pressure, heart diseases, insomnia and pneumonia. It should not be used in liver diseases.

Aniseed

Aniseed strengthens the process of digestion. It is very useful in dysentery, diarrhea, uterine ailments and is good for eyesight and for asthma.

Cardamom

Cardamom is a heart tonic. It relieves flatulence and strengthens digestion. It is very useful in nausea, cough and pains.

Cumin

Cumin is a good source of vitamin A and iron. It helps in digestion, urine production, cures colic, flatulence and increases appetite.

Sesame Seed

Sesame seed is a very good source of protein and is alkaline in nature. It contains calcium, iron and lecithin. It is used in the treatment of piles, anemia, bronchitis, pneumonia and asthma. It stimulates uterine contractions and thus helps in early termination of pregnancy. It is also beneficial in painful and scanty menstruation.

Onion Seed

Onion seed increases semen and is found to be beneficial in the treatment of dental worms and urinary disorders.

Tamarind

Its pulp is used in sunstrokes and is applied on the palms and the soles of feet at such times. It relieves heart-burn. It is good for digestion, and is an antiflatulent, antiseptic, and laxative.

Poppy Seed

This is effective in thirst, fever, inflammation and irritation of the stomach.

Cinnamon

It prevents nervous tension, improves complexion and memory.

9

High Fibre Chapatis

1. Stuffed Vegetable Chapatis

Ingredients	Quantity
Whole wheat flour	2 cups
Water	1 cup
For Stuffing	
vegetables like cauliflower, radish and carrot (finely grated)/boiled and mashed potatoes	2 cups
coriander leaves (finely chopped)	1 tbsp
red chilli powder	1/2 tsp
thyme	1/2 tsp

Method

(a) **Preparation of dough**—Knead whole wheat flour (2 cups) with water (about 1 cup).

(b) **Preparation of Stuffing**—Mix vegetables and potato with coriander leaves, red chilli powder, thyme and salt to taste.

(c) **Method of stuffing the chapati**—Divide the dough into small, even balls (about half the size of a lime). Roll out the balls to 2–3" diameter. Put 1 tbsp of stuffing at the centre of one such chapati. Spread the stuffing evenly and place another small chapati on top. Press the edges of the stuffed chapati, dust with wheat flour and roll lightly (6–7" diameter).

(d) **Making the chapati**—Bake on a frying pan (tava) without fat. Just before removing smear lightly with fresh cream or homemade butter.

Notes:

(i) Grated ginger can be added to cauliflower chapatis and finely chopped garlic to potato chapatis.

(ii) For cauliflower stuffing use cauliflower (1 cup), green coriander (finely chopped, $\frac{1}{2}$ to 1 cup), green chilli paste (to taste), Maharashtrian kala masala powder ($\frac{1}{2}$ tsp) mixed with salt is especially suitable.

2. Vegetable Chapatis

Ingredients	Quantity
Whole wheat flour	2 cups
or	
a mixture of whole Bengal gram flour and whole wheat flour	1 cup each
Any suitable vegetable* (grated/finely chopped)	2 cups
Coriander leaves (finely chopped)	1 tbsp
Thyme	$\frac{1}{2}$ tsp
Red chilli powder	$\frac{1}{2}$ tsp
Salt	to taste

Method

1. Mix flour and vegetables, coriander leaves, thyme, red chilli powder and salt and prepare dough.
2. Make chapatis and serve hot.

Suitable vegetables: Carrot, radish and its leaves, raw papaya, cabbage, cauliflower, fenugreek leaves, spinach, goosefoot white, onion, coriander leaves, beetroot, potato, cucumber, gourds, pre-boiled whole pulses or a paste of sprouted pulses, fresh (grated) coconut, ripe banana and ash gourd or its juice.

10

Snacks

1. Beaten Rice (Flattened Rice/Parched Rice) Snacks

For these snacks it is preferable to use the thin variety of beaten rice. If the thicker variety is used, adjust the soaking time, cooking time and water required.

(i) Beaten Rice Instant Snack

See Puffed Rice instant snacks in this chapter (pp. 211–13).

(ii) Beaten Rice Mixture with Curd (5 servings)

Ingredients	Quantity
Beaten rice (thin variety, preferably lightly roasted)	2 cups
Puffed rice	1 cup
Roasted groundnuts with skin	4–5
Oven-fried Bengal gram	1 tbsp
Fresh coconut (grated)	1 tbsp
Coriander leaves (finely chopped)	1–2 tbsp
Green chillies (pieces or paste)	1 tsp
Salt	to taste
Jaggery crumbled	$\frac{1}{2}$ to 1 tsp
Lime juice/grated raw mango	to taste
Soaked/split Bengal gram (optional)	1 tsp
Curd	to taste

Method

1. Mix all the ingredients well. There should be just enough curd to wet mixture. [Approx. 70 cal/serving]

(iii) Beaten Rice with Chutneys/Pickles

Mix with Chutneys or Pickles (see Puffed Rice Snacks with Chutneys/Pickles on pp. 211–13).

(iv) Beaten Rice Dhokla (5 servings)

Ingredients	Quantity
Beaten rice	2 cups
Curd	1½ to 2 cups
Salt	to taste
Turmeric powder	a pinch
Green chilli (finely chopped)	1 tsp
Coriander leaves (finely chopped)	2 tsp
Fresh coconut (grated)	2 tbsp
Seasoning	
Oil	½ tsp
Mustard	½ tsp
Asafoetida	a pinch
Curry leaves	6–8

Method

1. Mix beaten rice with curd, salt and turmeric powder.
2. Add green chilli and coriander leaves.
3. Steam in dhokla pan or idli plates for 5–10 minutes.
4. Remove immediately, transfer onto a plate, cool in the open or under a fan till completely cold.
5. Cut the dhokla cake into pieces, sprinkle with coconut, and add seasoning. [Approx. **85 cal/serving**]

(v) Maharashtrian Pohe (4 servings)

Ingredients	Quantity
Beaten rice	2 cups
Potato (finely diced)	1 cup
Green peas (shelled, optional)	½ cup
Onion (finely chopped)	½ cup
Salt	to taste
Turmeric powder	a pinch
Fresh coconut (grated)	1–2 tbsp (garnish)
Coriander leaves (finely chopped)	
Lime juice (optional)	to taste

Ingredients	Quantity
Seasoning	
Oil	1–2 tsp
Mustard	½ tsp
Cumin	¼ tsp
Asafoetida	a pinch
Green chilli (pieces)	1 tsp

Method

1. Wash and drain beaten rice and set aside for about 15–30 minutes.
2. Add potatoes, peas (optional) and onion to the seasoning.
3. Cover pan with a lid on which water is poured. Leave undisturbed for 5 minutes on low fire.
4. Stir once and cover and cook till done, sprinkling (if necessary) with a little water and adding more water on the lid.
5. Add salt, turmeric powder and the soaked beaten rice.
6. Mix well and leave on low fire for 5 minutes.
7. Garnish with coconut and coriander leaves and lime juice. [Approx. **70 cal/serving**]

Note: Other English vegetables like beans, carrot, cauliflower, cabbage and capsicum (finely chopped; 2 cups) can also be added.

(vi) Beaten Rice Sour and Dry Mixture

Ingredients	Quantity
Puffed rice	1 cup
Beaten rice	2 cups
Sesame seed	2 tsp
Groundnuts with skin	½ cup
Oven-fried Bengal gram (optional)	¼ cup
Seasoning	
Oil	1½ tsp
Mustard	1 tsp
Cumin	1 tsp
Asafoetida	a pinch
Green chilli (finely chopped)	1 tsp
Curry leaves	6–8
Onion (finely chopped)	¾ cup

Ingredients	Quantity
Ginger and/or garlic (paste)	1 tsp
Turmeric powder	¼ tsp
Red chilli powder	½ tsp
Jaggery (crumbled)	1 tsp
Lime juice	1–2 tbsp
Salt	to taste

Method

1. Separately dry roast, puffed rice, beaten rice, sesame seed and groundnuts until crisp.
2. To the seasoning add onion and ginger and/or garlic paste, turmeric powder, red chilli powder, jaggery, lime juice and salt.
3. Remove from fire and add roasted puffed rice, beaten rice, groundnuts and oven-fried Bengal gram and mix well. [Approx. **50 cal/serving**]

Note: The mixture becomes a little soggy especially after a day or two due to the small quantity of oil used for frying the onions. This is because the groundnuts, beaten rice, puffed rice etc. absorb moisture from the onions. To make the mixture crisp again pick out all the groundnuts and dry roast them till crisp. Dry roast the rest of the mixture on low fire till all the moisture evaporates and it becomes crisp again. Add the roasted groundnuts to the mixture again.

For a mixture which will stay crisp for longer, use 5–6 tbsp of oil for seasoning, fry the onions to redness, add lime juice, keep on low fire for a few seconds for the moisture in the lime juice to evaporate and then add the beaten rice, puffed rice and groundnuts.

(vii) Beaten Rice Dosa

See Dosas on p. 203 in this chapter.

(viii) Beaten Rice Curd Bhath (3 servings)

Ingredients	Quantity
Beaten rice	1 cup
Curd	2 cups
Salt	to taste
Fresh coconut (grated)	1 tsp

Ingredients	Quantity
Coriander leaves (finely chopped)	1 tbsp
raw/cooked vegetables like cucumber, cabbage, carrot, onion (grated/finely chopped)	to taste and nutritional requirement

Seasoning (optional)	
Ghee	$\frac{1}{2}$ tsp
Black gram	$\frac{1}{2}$ tsp
Mustard	$\frac{1}{2}$ tsp
Green chilli (chopped)	to taste
Curry leaves	2–4
Cumin	$\frac{1}{4}$ tsp
Ginger (pieces/paste) (optional)	$\frac{1}{2}$ tsp
Onion (finely chopped) (optional)	$\frac{1}{4}$ cup

Method 1

1. Wash and drain beaten rice.
2. Add curd and salt and add seasoning.
3. Keep aside for 10–15 minutes, until the beaten rice gets soaked. Garnish with coconut and coriander leaves.
4. Add vegetables, (to taste and nutritional requirements). [Approx. **85 cal/serving**]

Method 2

1. Add beaten rice to warm milk also adding salt and a little curd for curdling.
2. Allow mixture to stand till it sets (4–5 hours). It is tasty and can be eaten as it is.
3. The above seasoning and/or garnishing as in (1) may be added before or after the milk sets.

Note: The beaten rice need not be washed; the amount of curd can be adjusted to taste.

2. Bread Snack

Brown Bread Dahi Vada (4 servings)

Ingredients	Quantity
Brown bread (toasted slices)	4
Curd	2 cups

Ingredients	Quantity
Salt	to taste
Turmeric powder	a pinch
Coriander leaves (finely chopped)	2 tsp
Seasoning	
Oil	1 tsp
Black gram	1 tsp
Mustard	½ tsp
Cumin	¼ tsp
Green chilli (pieces/paste)	to taste
Onion (finely chopped)	2–3 tsp
Curry leaves	6–8
Asafoetida	a pinch

Method

1. Add the seasoning to curd.
2. Add salt, turmeric powder and coriander leaves, and mix well.
3. Dip toasted brown bread into the seasoned curd, one slice at a time for just a minute.
4. Serve immediately before bread becomes soggy. [Approx. **148** cal/serving]

3. Dosas with Pulses/Protein Dosas

(i) Black Gram (without skin) Dosas (10 servings)

Ingredients	Quantity
Black gram (without skin)	1 cup
Fenugreek seed	1 tsp
Bengal gram	1 tbsp
Water	2½ cups
Raw rice	4 cups
Water	3–4 cups

Method of preparing batter for dosas

1. Wash and soak black gram, fenugreek seed and Bengal gram.
2. Wash and soak raw rice for 3–6 hours. (In summer soaking for 2–3 hours is adequate.)
3. Grind the soaked black gram using the soaked water as required, into a thick, fine (rava), paste. If using a grinding

stone grind for 15–20 minutes. This helps in aerating the batter. The more aerated the batter, the softer (lighter) are the dosas/idlis. Set the batter aside.

4. Drain one cup of water from the soaked rice and grind the soaked rice with the remaining water into a thick fine (rava) paste.
5. Add salt and the pulse batter.
6. Mix thoroughly and set aside to ferment for 6–8 hours (depending on the season).

Method of making dosas

1. Grease a frying pan (*tava*) by putting a little oil onto the hot *tava* and sprinkling a little water on it. As the water vaporizes, it spreads the oil evenly on the *tava*. Note however that if too much oil is used to grease the *tava*, the dosa batter will not spread evenly and will form lumps.
2. Lower the heat and put a ladleful of the dosa batter onto the *tava*, spread evenly starting from the centre, add a little oil ($\frac{1}{4}$ tsp) at the edges and centre.
3. Keep for a minute, cook on moderate heat and turn dosa over.
4. Cook for a few seconds and remove.

Note: For crisp dosas, cook on low heat and/or add more oil. Adjust the consistency of the dosa batter for crispness. If the batter is very thick, the dosas will not be very crisp. However, if the batter is very thin, the dosa may stick to the *tava*. When storing, dosa batter should be thick. Diluted batter will turn sour very quickly. [Approx. **120 cal/serving**]

(ii) Black Gram (with skin) Dosas

Ingredients	Quantity
Black gram (whole or split) with skin	1 cup
Water	2 cups

Method

Dosas and idlis made from black gram with skin are softer and tastier. Black gram with skin is soaked in water and the skin is removed by hand as given in the note on Ash gourd vadas (p. 102).

Use this skinned black gram (using 2 to 2½ cups of the soaked water for grinding) to make the dosas. The skin should be used as given in recipe (ii) of Ash gourd on p. 102.

Other Proportions of Pulses and Rice for Dosas

Note:
For soaking

> 1 cup black gram, use 2 cups water. Remove a little water when grinding and add it later if necessary.
> 1 cup raw rice, use 1 cup water.
> 1 cup boiled rice, use 1¼ cups water.

Remove a little water (say ½ cup) and add it later if necessary while grinding or for thinning the batter while making the dosas.

(a)

Ingredients		Quantity
Black gram		1 cup
Fenugreek seed	soak together	1 tsp
Bengal gram		1 tblsp
Water		2 to 2 ½ cups
Raw rice	soak	2 cups
Water		2 cups

Dosas made with these proportions have a flavour and taste of black gram and are soft and spongy.

(b)

Ingredients		Quantity
Black gram		1 cup
Fenugreek seed	soak together	1 tsp
Water		2 cups
Raw rice		2 cups
Boiled rice	soak together	1 cup
Beaten rice		1 tblsp
Water		3 cups

Dosas made with these proportions are soft and spongy:

(c)

Ingredients		Quantity
Black gram		1 cup
Fenugreek seed		½ tsp
Bengal gram	soak together	1 tbsp
Green gram		1 tbsp
Water		2–2½ cups

(c)

Ingredients		Quantity
Raw rice	soak together	3 cups
Cooked rice		1 cup
Water		3½–4 cups

Dosas made with these proportions are spongy and crisp and are slightly sweet and have a reddish tinge.

(d)

Ingredients		Quantity
Black gram	soak together	1 cup
Fenugreek seed		½ tsp
Green gram		1 tbsp
Bengal gram		
Water		2–2½ cups
Raw rice	soak together	3 cups
Cooked rice		1 cup
Beaten rice		2 tbsp
Water		3½–4 cups

Note: Fenugreek, beaten rice and cooked rice give a sweetish taste and softness to the dosas.

Common Batter for Dosas and Idlis

Ingredients		Quantity
Black gram	soak together	1 cup
Fenugreek seed		½ tsp
Water		2 cups
Boiled rice	soak together	2 cups
Raw rice		2 cups
Water		5 cups

(iii) Vegetable Dosas with the Dosa Batter (2 servings)

Ingredients	Quantity
Dosa batter	1 cup
Grated vegetables like cauliflower/ cabbage/ridge gourd/ smooth gourd/bottle gourd/ cucumber/brinjal etc.	1 cup
Green chilli (paste)	1 tsp

Method

1. Add grated vegetables, salt, green chilli paste to the dosa batter (slightly thick), mix well and make dosas.

2. These dosas cannot be made very thin. [Approx. **95 cal/ serving**]

Notes:

a) Whole wheat flour can also be added to the batter especially when the batter is thinner than required
b) When watery vegetables like ridge and smooth gourd are added, the dosa batter must be thicker because the vegetables also add their own water content.
c) Add finely chopped onion, coriander leaves, curry leaves and green chilli paste to taste.

(iv) Dosas with Rice Flour (instead of rice)

Ingredients	Quantity
Rice flour	3 cups
Water	2 cups
Black gram	1 cup ground with 2 cups of water

Method

1. Moisten the rice flour. Add exactly 2 cups of water to the rice flour (3 cups) and leave to soak for ½–1 hour. Alternatively, soak 3 cups rice flour in 6 cups water for 2–3 hours, decant the water and use this rice flour.
2. Add this rice flour to very finely ground black gram batter, mix well and ferment for 3–4 hours depending on the season.
3. The batter may require thinning if made from rice flour soaked in just sufficient water. However the batter obtained when water is decanted from soaked rice flour is quite thin.
4. Make dosas. If a non-stick frying pan is used, the dosas come out very crisp.

(v) Green Gram Dosas (Pesarattu) (4 servings)

Ingredients		Quantity
Green gram with skin (whole or split)	soak together	1 cup
Raw		¼ cup
Water		1¾ cups

Ingredients	Quantity
Onion (1 cm cubes) (optional)	½ cup
Ginger	½" piece
Green chilli	2 or 3
For sprinkling on the dosa:	
Green chilli (very finely chopped)	1 tsp
Ginger (very finely chopped)	2 tsp
Onion (finely chopped)	2 cups
Cumin	1 tsp

Method

1. Soak green gram and raw rice in water.
2. Grind into a very fine paste with onion, ginger and green chilli, using the water used for soaking for grinding.
3. Dilute the batter if necessary and spread a ladleful on a hot greased frying pan to make a thin dosa.
4. Sprinkle 1–2 tbsp of finely chopped mixture made from green chilli, ginger, onion and cumin. Press a little with the ladle, so that the mixture gets slightly embedded in the dosa.
5. When one side of the dosa is done, turn over carefully. When it is roasted enough, remove from pan. These dosas are delicious when hot and are a speciality of Andhra Pradesh. [Approx. **100 cal/serving**]

Note: Grated vegetables (½ cup) like cabbage or cauliflower can also be added to the batter (1 cup). Raw rice can be completely omitted, in which case the dosa batter (made from 1 cup green gram and 1½ cups water) must have a thicker consistency. Without rice the dosas will be much softer. Serve hot.

(vi) *Bottle Gourd/Ridge Gourd/Tinda/Parwal (unpeeled and with seeds) Dosas (5 servings)*

Ingredients	Quantity
Rice	1 cup
Black gram (preferably with skin)	2 tbsp
Water	1 cup
Bottle gourd/ridge gourd (grated)	4 cups
Salt	to taste
Green chilli	3–4

Method

1. Wash and soak rice and black gram in water.
2. Drain the water and grind with grated bottle gourd/ridge gourd, salt and green chilli into a fine paste (dosa consistency).
3. Make dosas with or without fermenting the batter.
4. If dosas are made without fermenting the batter, a little sour curd can be added for sourness. [Approx. **145 cal/serving**]

Note: Grate the bottle gourd/ridge gourd (even if it is not very tender) along with its peel and seeds. If these vegetables are quite hard the peel and seeds can be removed and ground with the pulses and rice. The peeled vegetables can be used for making curries.

4. Dosas without Pulses/Non-Protein Dosas

(i) Whole Wheat Flour Dosas with the White Portion of the Water Melon or other Vegetables, their peels seeds (4 servings)

Ingredients		Quantity
Bottle gourd/ridge gourd/parwal/ cucumber/tinda	grated or ground	1 cup
Whole wheat flour and rice flour or		½ cup each
Wheat flour		1 cup
Salt		to taste
Green chilli (paste)		1 tsp
Onion (finely cut or grated, optional)		¼ cup
Coriander leaves (finely cut, optional)		1 tsp
Sour curd/buttermilk		to taste

Method

1. Peel the bottle gourd/ridge gourd/parwal/cucumber/tinda with a fine peeler. (If the peel is thin it is not necessary to grind it for making dosas. If it is thick, it should be ground in a mixie.
2. Use the (grated or ground) vegetable peel to make dosas.
3. Alternatively, grate or grind the whole vegetable along with its peel and seeds. Add rice flour and/or wheat flour, salt, green chilli and onion to taste and coriander leaves (optional).

4. Mix thoroughly into a slightly thicker consistency than dosa batter, adding a little water or sour curd/buttermilk if necessary. The curd gives extra taste and flavour.
5. Spread on a hot greased frying pan, keep on medium or low fire and make the dosas as usual using a few drops of oil. These dosas are soft and not too thin. [Approx. **110 cal/serving**]

Suitable vegetables: Bottle gourd, ridge gourd, smooth gourd, brinjal, cabbage, cauliflower, cucumber, carrot, pumpkin, white portion of water melon.

To make **dosas** with the **white portion of water melon**, remove the red portion. Grate the white portion just below the skin with a fine grater. Alternatively, cut the white portion into pieces and coarsely grind in a mixie. Use this to make soft delicious dosas as given above.

Notes:

a) Vegetables like bottle gourd, ridge gourd and smooth gourd give off a lot of water when grated. To such vegetables, add flour till the correct consistency of batter is obtained. Do not add extra water. Alternatively, water from the vegetables can be used for gravies. The vegetable can then be used, in which case less flour will be needed.
b) Rice flour can be omitted and just whole wheat flour can be used.
c) Flour of sprouted pulses can also be added to make the dosas more nutritious.
d) see p. 203 (vii) for dosas made with leftover wheat fibre.

(ii) Corn Dosas (3 servings)

Ingredients	Quantity
Corn	2 cobs
Green chilli	2
rice flour/soaked rice	1 tbsp

Method

1. Grate or take out the pearls (2 cups) of the corn.
2. Add green chilli, soaked rice or rice flour and water as required. Grind into a fine paste.

3. Make dosas as above and serve hot. (When cold the dosas harden a little.) [Approx. **110 cal/serving**]
4. Finely chopped onion, coriander leaves and curry leaves can be added to the batter for softness and taste or add 2 tbsp of soaked black gram while grinding the corn.

(iii) Tomato Dosas (8 servings)

Ingredients	Quantity
Whole wheat flour	1 cup
rice flour	1 cup
Green chilli (pieces/paste)	1 tsp
Water	1 cup or as required
Onion (finely chopped)	½ cup
Curry leaves (finely chopped)	1 tsp
Coriander leaves (finely chopped)	1 tbsp
Tomato (1 cm cubes)	1 cup
Salt	to taste

Method

1. Make a batter of whole wheat flour, rice flour, salt, green chilli and water.
2. Add onion, curry leaves, coriander leaves and tomato.
3. Mix well, crushing the tomato in this process. If a predominantly sour taste is preferred, add more tomato.
4. The batter should not be thin like that of black gram dosas.
5. The dosas will be a little thick.
6. Make dosas without fermenting the batter on moderate or low heat. [Approx. **94 cal/serving**]

Note: The tomato can be coarsely blended in the mixie. Rice flour can be omitted and 2 cups whole wheat flour can be used instead.

(iv) Sour Curd/Buttermilk Dosas

Ingredients	Quantity
Sour curd/buttermilk	1 cup/2 cups
Water (only if curd is used)	1 cup
Any vegetable like bottle gourd/ridge gourd/smooth gourd/ cucumber (grated)	1 cup
Salt	to taste

Ingredients	Quantity
Whole wheat flour and rice flour, or only whole wheat flour	1½ cup
Green chilli paste	1 tsp
Cumin	½ tsp
Coriander leaves (finely chopped)	1 tbsp
Onion (finely chopped, optional)	1 tbsp

Method

1. To sour curd add water, flour, green chilli paste, cumin, coriander leaves and onion.
2. Mix well to a moderate consistency, adding grated vegetable (and water if necessary).
3. Make dosas as described above. [Approx. **100 cal/serving**]

Notes:

a) These dosas cannot be spread very thin, especially when onion is added.
b) If the curd or buttermilk is not sour, add a little lime juice to the curd or leave the batter to ferment for a few hours.
c) The quantity and sourness of the curd can be varied to taste.

(v) Yam Dosas (3 servings)

Ingredients	Quantity
Yam (grated)	1 cup
Rice	
or	1 tbsp
Whole wheat flour/soaked raw rice	
Green chilli	1 or 2
Cumin	½ tsp
Onion (finely chopped)	½ cup
Water	2 tbsp
Soaked green gram with skin/red gram	1 tbsp

Method

1. Grind yam and rice/whole wheat flour/raw rice into a fine paste with green chilli, cumin, onion and water.
2. Make dosas as above, adding as much water as necessary.
3. The taste can be enhanced by adding soaked green gram (with

skin) or red gram when grinding the batter [Approx. **115 cal/ serving**]

Note: Grated vegetable and finely chopped onion can also be added to the batter. Rice flour/rice/whole wheat flour can be omitted completely and dosas made with yam only.

(vi) Beaten Rice Dosas (16 servings)

Ingredients	Quantity
Beaten rice	1 cup
Raw rice	3 cups
Curd	1 cup
Water	2–2½ cups
Fenugreek seed	1 tsp
Salt	to taste
Green chilli	1 or 2

Method

1. Wash and soak fenugreek seed, beaten rice and raw rice in curd and water.
2. Grind into a paste with salt and green chilli.
3. Leave to ferment for 3–4 hours and then make dosas adding a little water (½ cup or so) if needed.
4. Do not use a thick batter since it is difficult to spread. These dosas should preferably be spread on low heat first and then baked on high heat till done.
5. Serve hot. When cold and made on low heat they harden especially when the batter is thick. [Approx. **95 cal/serving**]

Note: Grated vegetable can also be added to the batter.

(vii) Bran Dosas (high fibre) (5 servings)

Ingredients	Quantity
Wheat bran/rice bran/wheat skins[*]	3 tbsp
Whole wheat flour	6 tbsp
Rice flour (optional)	1 tbsp
Green chilli paste	to taste

*See page no. 275 for wheat skin (Point no. 5).

Ingredients	Quantity
Vegetables like cabbage/cauliflower/ ridge gourd/smooth gourd/cucumber/bottle gourd/brinjal/chow-chow (finely grated)	3–6 tbsp
Curd	1–2 tbsp
Salt	to taste
Cumin	½ tsp
Water	½ cup

Method

1. Mix bran, flour, green chilli paste, grated vegetables, curd, salt, cumin and water into the desired consistency.
2. Make dosas on *tava*, on low fire. [Approx. 90 cal/serving]

Notes:

a) Grate the vegetables very finely so that the batter is smooth and the vegetables blend well.
b) The batter should be a little thicker than the usual dosa batter.
c) Finely grated vegetable peel or finely ground paste of vegetable peel can also be added for enhanced nutritional value.

(viii) Lady's Fingers/Ash Gourd Dosas (9 servings)

Ingredients		Quantity
Rice	⎫	3 cups
Fenugreek seed	⎬ wash and soak	½ tsp
Water	⎭	3 cups
Lady's fingers		few pieces
or		
Ash gourd (1 cm cubes)		3 cups
Salt		to taste

Method

1. Wash and soak rice and fenugreek seed in water for 2–3 hours.
2. Add vegetables and grind into a fine consistency using all the water used for soaking.
3. Add salt, allow the batter to ferment and make dosas. [Approx. **122 cal/serving**]

Note: Add green chilli paste (2 tsp) and about 3 cups finely grated vegetables like bottle gourd or chow-chow (with peel) especially when lady's fingers are used. These vegetables make the dosas softer.

5. High Fibre Chutney and Powder for Dosas/Idlis

(i) High Fibre Chutney

Ingredients	Quantity
Bottle gourd with peel	$\frac{1}{2}$ kg
Water	1 $\frac{1}{2}$ cups
Fresh coconut (grated)	1$\frac{1}{2}$ cups
Oven fried/roasted Bengal gram (powdered)	2 tbsp
Curd	2 tbsp
Green chilli	4
Salt	to taste
Seasoning	
Oil	1 tsp
Mustard	1 tsp
Coriander leaves (finely chopped)	6–8

Method

1. Cook bottle gourd in water.
2. Cool and add coconut, oven-fried /roasted Bengal gram powder, curd, green chillies and salt.
3. Grind into a fine paste and season.

(ii) High Fibre Powder of Pumpkin/Musk Melon Seeds

Ingredients	Quantity
Pumpkin seeds/musk melon seeds	1 cup
Red chilli	1 or 2
Salt	to taste

Method

1. Wash and dry the seeds thoroughly. Dry roast the seeds and red chilli. Powder with salt and sieve. Most of the husk will be left in the sieve. Grind this husk again and sieve. Repeat the process until the husk cannot be ground any further. At

this stage, mix this husk with the sieved powder. The husk adds to the fibre content. This powder is a nutritious high-fibre powder. It has a very pleasant aroma and goes well with pulaos, plain rice, idlis and dosas.

(iii) Coriander leaf—fresh coconut chutney for idlis and dosas (low calorie, highly nutritious) with all ingredients—see p. 237.

6. Idlis

Idlis made from black gram with skin are softer. See p. 194 (ii). For high fibre chutney and powder see pp. 236, 237, 205.

(i) Plain Idlis (20 servings)

Ingredients		Quantity
Black gram	} soaked	1 cup
Fenugreek seed		½ tsp
Water		2 –2½ cups
Boiled rice	} soaked	3 cups
Water		4½ cups

Method

1. Wash and soak black gram and fenugreek seed in one pan and boiled rice in another for 4–8 hours depending on the weather (soak longer in winter).
2. Grind the soaked black gram with the water used for soaking until finely ground. Continue grinding for 15–20 minutes to aerate it well. The batter will become very light and frothy. Set aside.
3. Grind the rice with the water used for soaking into a coarse rava consistency.
4. Add salt and black gram batter, mix well and set aside until it ferments.
5. Add enough water to make the batter of pouring consistency.
6. Steam in idli plates for 6–8 minutes.
7. The idlis will be very light, soft and spongy. If the batter is thick, the idlis will be hard. If it is too thin the idlis will be

soggy. A little practice will yield good results. [Approx. **85 cal/serving**]

(ii) Vegetable Idlis (3 servings)

Ingredients	Quantity
Cauliflower or cabbage (finely grated)	1 cup
Idli batter	1 cup
Salt	to taste

Method

Add grated cauliflower or cabbage to idli batter, salt, mix well and steam for a little longer than for normal idlis since these take longer to cook. [Approx. **58 cal/serving**]

Notes:
a) The proportion of grated vegetable to batter can be varied to taste.
b) Green chilli paste, onion, coriander leaves, asafoetida (optional) can also be added.
c) The batter should be slightly thick.
d) Finely shredded English vegetables can be added to the batter instead of grated vegetables. Water will ooze out if vegetables like gourds or cucumber are grated, but this will not happen when they are finely shredded.

Most suitable vegetables: cauliflower, cabbage, carrot and beans.

(iii) Idlis with Rava of Boiled Rice (16 servings)

Ingredients	Quantity
Black gram ⎫ soaked	1 cup
Fenugreek seed ⎬	½ tsp
Water ⎭	2½–3 cups
Boiled rice rava ⎫ soaked	3 cups
Water ⎭	2 cups

Method

1. Wash and soak black gram and fenugreek seed.
2. Soak boiled rice rava in just enough water to wet it for 30–45 minutes.

3. Grind the black gram with the water into a very fine consistency and add the rava* and salt.
4. Grind this batter for just a minute or keep it as it is. Ferment and make idlis. [Approx. **87 cal/serving**]

Note: Although idlis are easy to digest, they can be made even more digestible if the rice is roasted to mild redness before it is soaked in water.

Other Proportions of Black Gram and Rice for Idlis

(i) Ingredients	Quantity
Black gram	1 cup
Fenugreek seed } soaked	½ tsp
Water	2½ cups
Boiled rice or its rava	2 cups
Water } soaked	5 cups
ii) **Black gram**	1 cup
Fenugreek seed } soaked	½ tsp
Water	2½ cups
Boiled rice	2 cups
Raw rice } soaked	2 cups
Water	5 cups

The black gram batter can be preserved in a refrigerator, the rava* (soaked for an hour before mixing) added when required and the batter fermented.

7. Uttappams

(i) Flat Uttappams (3 servings)

Ingredients	Quantity
Idli batter	1 cup
Vegetables like cauliflower/cabbage/carrot (grated)	1 cup
Green chilli (paste)	1 tsp

---

*Instead of soaking the rava add 6–8 cups water to the rava, mix thoroughly and immediately drain the water through a strainer. Use this wet rava immediately as it does not need soaking.

Ingredients	Quantity
Salt	to taste
Onion (finely chopped, optional)	¼ cup
Curry leaves (finely chopped)	1 tsp
Coriander leaves (finely chopped, optional)	1 tsp

Method

1. Use slightly thick idli batter.
2. Add grated vegetables, green chilli, salt, onion, curry leaves, coriander leaves and mix well.
3. Pour a ladleful onto a greased non-stick *tava* and spread (to 1 cm thickness), add oil on the sides, cover with a lid, and turn over when done. Cook again till this side is done. Top with pieces of tomato soon after pouring the batter. [Approx. 101 cal/serving]

(ii) Golf Balls/Round Uttappams

Pour spoonfuls of the above batter into heated, greased, round uttappam moulds, cover with a plate for a few seconds, turn over and cook till golden.

8. Potato Snack

Potato Chops (4 servings)

Ingredients	Quantity
For the Stuffing:	
Potato (boiled and mashed)	2 cups
Oil	1 tsp
Onion (finely chopped)	½ cup
Coriander leaves (finely chopped)	1 cup
Tomato (finely chopped)	½ cup
Turmeric powder	a pinch
Maharashtrian kala masala powder	1 tsp
Red chilli powder/green chilli (paste)	1 tsp
Salt	to taste
For the Batter:	
Whole wheat flour	1 cup

Ingredients	Quantity
Rice flour (optional)	½ cup
Water	1–½ cups
Salt	to taste
Red chilli powder/green chilli paste	1 tsp

Method

1. Boil and mash potato.
2. Fry onion, coriander and tomato in oil till cooked.
3. Add all the other ingredients of the stuffing and mix well:
4. Make 8 even-sized balls and flatten.
5. Make a thin batter of flour, water, salt, and chilli.
6. Dip the flattened balls into the batter and shallow fry on a non-stick *tava* in ½ tsp oil till golden brown on both sides. [Approx. 75 cal/serving]

Note: Omit Maharashtrian kala masala powder or add garam masala powder, roasted coriander seed and roasted cumin powder. Cooked English vegetables like beans, carrot (1 cup or more) can also be added to the mashed potato.

9. Puffed Rice Snacks

These snacks must be eaten immediately because they become soggy very quickly.

(i) Puffed Rice Bhel

Ingredients	Quantity
Puffed rice	4 cups
Sev (thin variety)	¼ cup
Roasted groundnuts	10
Ghatias (ridge shaped sev, 1 cm pieces)	¼ cup
Papdi (flat sev, 1 cm pieces)	¼ cup
Tomato (finely chopped)	5–6 tbsp
Onion (finely chopped)	5–6 tbsp
Coriander leaves (finely chopped)	5–6 tbsp
Tamarind paste/finely grated raw mango	3–4 tsp

Method

1. Mix crisp puffed rice, sev, groundnuts, ghatias and papdi together.
2. Add tomato, onion and green coriander leaves.
3. Add tamarind paste and/or finely grated raw mango to taste and mix well. Serve immediately before it becomes soggy. [Approx. **50 cal/serving**]

Tamarind Paste

Ingredients	Quantity
Oil	1 tsp
Ginger (paste)	1 tsp
Green chilli (paste)	1 tsp
Thick tamarind extract	½ cup
Jaggery	1½ to 2 lime-sized balls (or as per taste)
Water	1 cup
Roasted cumin (powdered)	1 tsp
Salt	to taste

Method

1. Fry ginger and green chilli paste.
2. When it is lightly fried and gives off a good aroma, add a thick extract of tamarind, jaggery, water, roasted cumin and salt.
3. Boil till mixture thickens and halves in volume.
4. Bottle when cold.

(ii) Instant Puffed Rice with Chutney or Pickle

Ingredients	Quantity
Puffed rice or beaten rice	2 cups
Oil	1 tsp
Pickle/long standing chutney	1 tsp or as per taste

Add oil to the puffed rice and then mix in pickle or long standing chutney or fresh chutney of coconut, green coriander or carrot. *A few chutneys are given below:*

(a) Green Coriander Chutney

Ingredients	Quantity
Fresh coconut (grated)	¼–½ cup
Coriander leaves (finely chopped)	2 cups
Green chilli	2
Cumin	¼ tsp
Onion (finely chopped, optional)	1–2 tbsp
Salt	to taste

Method

1. Coarsely grind together all the ingredients (except cumin).
2. Cumin must be added almost at the end of the grinding process.

(b) Curry Powder Chutney

Ingredients	Quantity
Onion (coarsely grated)	1–2 tbsp
Curry powder	1 tbsp
Fresh coconut (grated)	½–1 tbsp
Green chilli (optional)	1
Salt	to taste

Method

1. Add onion to curry powder, coconut, green chilli (optional), salt and mix well.
2. Instead of grating onion and fresh coconut, finely chop and then coarsely grind them with curry powder, green chilli and salt.

(c) Mint (Pudina) Chutney – see p. 240.

(d) Tomato Chutney – see p. 243.

(e) Coconut-Onion Chutney – see p. 237.

(f) Raw Onion–Coconut Paste

Ingredients	Quantity
Fresh coconut (grated)	2 tbsp
Raw onion (1 cm cubes)	¾ cup
Green chilli	2
cumin	1 tsp
Salt	to taste

Method

Grind together all the ingredients coarsely.

(iii) Instant Puffed Rice with Curd

Add Puffed Rice to any Raita (pp. 246–48) or to Plain salted curd.

(iv) Instant Puffed Rice with Tomato, Onion and Coriander leaves (2 servings)

Ingredients	Quantity
Onion (finely chopped)	
Tomato (finely chopped)	total ½ cup
Coriander leaves (finely chopped)	
Green chilli (paste)	1 tsp
Thick tamarind paste* or	
Raw mango (grated)	1–2 tsp
Puffed rice	2 cups

Method

Mix all the ingredients together. [Approx. 75 cal/serving]

(v) Maharashtrian Style Puffed Rice Mixture (shallow fried) (8 servings)

Ingredients	Quantity
Puffed rice	2 cups
Oil	1 tbsp
Beaten rice	½ cup
Groundnuts (with skin)	12–18
Seasoning:	
Oil	2 tbsp
Mustard	½ tsp
Cumin	½ tsp
Aniseed (optional)	½ tsp
Green chilli (paste/pieces)	1 tsp
Onion (finely chopped)	2 tbsp
Garlic (crushed)	2–3 flakes
Dry coconut (grated)	1–2 tbsp
Curry leaves (finely chopped)	12 to 15

*See page 211.

Ingredients	Quantity
Lime juice	1–2 tsp
Salt	to taste
Turmeric powder	½ tsp
Sugar or jaggery powder	1 tsp

Method

1. Sun-dry puffed rice till crisp or dry roast without oil (on very low heat) stirring constantly.
2. Roast beaten rice on low fire until crisp.
3. Dry roast groundnuts.
4. To hot oil, add mustard, cumin, aniseed, green chilli, onion, garlic and fry till pink.
5. Add coconut, curry leaves, lime juice ,salt, turmeric powder, sugar or jaggery powder, roasted groundnuts and roasted crisp puffed rice and beaten rice.
6. Mix well and cool.
7. Preserve in an airtight container when thoroughly cooled. [Approx. **40 cal/serving**]

(vi) Puffed Rice with Maharashtrian Kala Masala Powder

Ingredients	Quantity
Oil	1–2 tsp
Curry leaves	20–25
Salt	to taste
Red chilli powder	½ tsp
Turmeric powder	¼ tsp
Maharashtrian kala masala powder	¼ tsp
Puffed rice	4 cups

Method

1. Add curry leaves to hot oil, fry and remove.
2. Add salt, red chilli powder, turmeric powder, Maharashtrian kala masala powder to the oil. Remove from fire.
3. Add fried curry leaves and puffed rice and mix well. [Approx. **31 cal/serving**]

Note: To the above, add boondi (½ cup), mixture (½ cup), roasted groundnuts (24), fried dry coconut slices (2 tsp), and fried curry leaves. Instead of Maharashtrian kala masala powder, add a little garam masala powder and powder of roasted cumin and coriander.

(vii) Seasoned Puffed Rice (3 servings)

Ingredients	Quantity
Puffed rice	2 cups
Turmeric powder	a pinch
Seasoning:	
Oil	1 tsp
Mustard	½ tsp
Garlic (coarsely ground)	½ tsp
Roasted groundnuts (with skin)	10–12
Bengal gram (oven fried)	1 tsp
Salt	to taste
Green chilli (pieces or paste)/red chilli powder	to taste

Method

1. Season mustard and garlic.
2. Add groundnuts, Bengal gram, and chilli paste/ powder.
3. Add salt, puffed rice and turmeric powder. Mix well and remove from fire.
4. Powdered aniseed, cumin, sugar/jaggery can be added to taste. [Approx. 45 cal/serving]

10. Semolina (Suji) Snacks

(i) Vegetable Rava Upma (either rice or whole wheat rava) (4 servings)

Ingredients	Quantity
Any English vegetable alone or in combination [(capsicum, carrot, cabbage, green peas, cauliflower and beans (finely diced)]	1–2 cups
Rava/semolina	1 cup
Salt	to taste
Seasoning:	
Oil	1 tsp
Bengal gram	½ tsp

Ingredients	Quantity
Black gram	1 tsp
Mustard	1 tsp
Ginger (finely chopped/coarsely pounded)	1/2 tsp
Green chilli (finely chopped/coarsely pounded)	1/2 tsp
Curry leaves (finely chopped)	1 tsp
Onion (finely chopped)	1 tbsp
Mixed vegetables (finely diced)	1–2 cups
Water	2 cups

Method

1. Dry roast the rava/semolina till pink.
2. To hot oil, add Bengal gram, black gram, mustard, ginger, green chilli, curry leaves and onion and mixed vegetables.
3. Keep on low fire for a few minutes, stirring intermittently.
4. Cover pan with a lid on which water is poured.
5. When fried, add water, and salt and boil.
6. Add the roasted rava/suji/dalia and mix thoroughly.
7. Cover and keep on low fire for 3–5 minutes. [Approx. **125 cal/serving**]

Note: Pre-cooked vegetables can be used instead of raw vegetables. Add them when the rava is almost cooked and mix.

(ii) Semolina with Tamarind Extract (Pulihara) (4 servings)

Ingredients	Quantity
Semolina or rava of whole wheat	1 cup
Water	2 cups
Oil	1 tbsp
Salt	to taste
Turmeric powder	a pinch
Cabbage (finely sliced) (optional)	1 cup
Pulihara masala	2 tbsp
Roasted sesame seed (powder) (optional)	2 tsp
Sprouted pulses e.g. Bengal gram (pre-cooked)	2 tbsp

For Pulihara Masala

Ingredients	Quantity
Oil	1 tsp

Ingredients	Quantity
Bengal gram	½ tsp
Black gram	1 tsp
Mustard	½ tsp
Green chilli (chopped or paste)	¼ tsp
Ginger (chopped or paste)	¼ tsp
Curry leaves	6–8
Groundnuts (with skin)	6–8
Thick tamarind extract	1½ tbsp

To hot oil, add Bengal gram, black gram, mustard, green chilli, ginger, curry leaves, groundnuts and thick tamarind extract and boil till it thickens and is almost dry.

Method

1. Add oil, salt, turmeric powder, and cabbage to boiling water and cook on low fire.
2. When half-cooked, add semolina or whole wheat rava, stir and cook on low fire.
3. Remove, spread on a plate (if it is soggy), add pulihara masala and mix well.
4. Add powdered roasted sesame seed and/or pre-cooked sprouted pulses like Bengal gram. [Approx. 141 cal/serving]

(iii) Semolina/Raw Rice Rava Uppupindi (4 servings)

Ingredients	Quantity
Raw rice rava/ semolina	1 cup
Mixed English vegetables (finely diced)	1 cup
Green peas (optional)	½ cup
Water	2 cups
Salt	to taste
Fresh coconut (grated) (garnish)	2 tbsp
Seasoning:	
Oil	2 tsp
Black gram	1 tsp
Cumin	½ tsp
Red/green chillies	2
Asafoetida	a pinch
Curry leaves	6–8

Method

1. Cook vegetables in minimum water.
2. Add water and salt to the seasoning and boil for 5 minutes.
3. Add raw rice rava or semolina and cooked vegetables and mix well. Cook on low flame for 5–10 minutes, covering pan with a plate.
4. Garnish with grated coconut. [Approx. **133 cal/serving**]

Notes:

a) Soaked green/Bengal gram (split, with or without skin), or sprouted green gram (¼ cup) added to the boiling water and cooked till done, adds richness and a good taste.
b) Cooked pulses can be used instead of raw pulses.
c) Instead of semolina/raw rice, whole wheat rava can be used.
d) Instead of water, churned sour curd (1 cup) and water (1 cup) can be used.

11. Spinach Snack

Spinach Gatta with Gram Flour (4 servings)

Ingredients	Quantity
Bengal gram flour	1 cup
Spinach (finely chopped)	1½ cups
Oil	1 tsp
Curd	¼–½ cup
Red chilli powder	½ tsp
Garam masala powder	¼ tsp
Salt	to taste
Seasoning:	
Oil	1 tsp
Mustard	½ tsp
Fenugreek seeds (optional)	½ tsp
Red chilli powder	¼ tsp
Any chutney	as accompaniment

Method

1. Mix flour, spinach, oil, curd, red chilli powder, garam masala powder and salt into a dough.

2. Roll by hand to form 1" long, 1cm diameter cylindrical rolls.
3. Boil water in a pan, place a sieve over it and arrange the rolls on the sieve.
4. Steam these rolls for 10–12 minutes and then cool.
5. Cut the rolls into small slices. If they crumble when sliced, steam them for a few minutes more.
6. Add the slices to a seasoning of mustard, fenugreek seeds (optional), red chilli powder, and cook for 3–4 minutes on low fire.
7. Serve hot with any chutney. These gattas can also be added to gravies. [Approx. **135 cal/serving**]

Note: Do not throw away the water used for steaming. Use it for soups or gravies.

12. Vegetable Fritters (Bajjis)

Bajjis of Brinjal, Ridge Gourd or Smooth Gourd on Tava (Frying Pan) without Deep Frying

Although these fritters do not taste the same as deep fried ones, they can be made tasty (with practice). Round brinjal with fewer seeds is more suitable. Ridge gourd should be smoothened a little so that the ridges are not rough enough to hurt the delicate lining of the mouth.

Ingredients	Quantity
Brinjal/ridge gourd/smooth gourd (unpeeled) (½ cm thick slices)	½ kg
For the batter	
Whole wheat flour	1 cup
Rice flour	1 cup
Green chilli paste	1–1½ tsp
Ginger paste	1–1½ tsp
Salt	to taste
Water	2½ cups
Oil	2–3 tsp

Method

1. Wash and cut vegetables into slices and set aside.

2. Mix flour, green chilli paste, ginger paste, salt, and water into a thinner consistency than usual. Whole wheat flour alone or wheat flour and other cereal flour can also be used.
3. Heat a frying pan and grease it. Dip each slice of vegetable in the batter and arrange them in the pan.
4. Add oil (¼ tsp) around the slices at the circumference.
5. Cover pan with a plate and keep for 2–3 minutes on a moderately hot flame.
6. Remove the cover and pierce a slice with spoon. If it is soft, it is cooked. Turn slices over.
7. Keep pan uncovered for a minute or two till the slices turn light brown. Remove, and serve hot. [Approx. **890 cal/serving**]

12. Vermicelli Snacks

(i) Vermicelli Pulao (8 servings)

Ingredients	Quantity
Vermicelli	2 cups
Oil	2 tsp
Water	2 cups
Salt	to taste
Seasoning:	
Oil	1 tbsp
Turmeric powder	a pinch
Asafoetida	¼ tsp
Cashew nuts	12
Raisins	12
Onion (finely chopped)/sesame seed	1 cup/1 tsp
Carrot,	
Cabbage	
Cauliflower,	¼ cup each
Beans	(finely sliced/grated)
Capsicum	
Green peas (shelled)	
Salt	to taste
Jaggery powder (optional)	¼ tsp
Lime juice	1 tbsp

Ingredients	Quantity
Coriander leaves (finely chopped)	1 tbsp
Fresh coconut (grated)	1 tbsp

garnish

Method

1. Roast vermicelli in oil.
2. Boil water with salt in a pan. Add vermicelli and cook till done.
3. To a seasoning of turmeric powder, asafoetida, cashew nuts, raisins, onion or sesame seed, add par-boiled or steamed vegetables, green chilli pieces and/or red chilli powder (in this order) and fry with salt and jaggery till done.
4. Mix with cooked vermicelli and keep on low fire for a few minutes and remove.
5. Add lime juice and mix well.
6. Garnish with coriander leaves and coconut. [Approx. 141 cal/serving]

Note: The amount of water needed for cooking vermicelli depends on its thickness; the thicker it is, the more water it needs.

(ii) Vermicelli Curd Bhaath (4 servings)

Ingredients	Quantity
Vermicelli	1 cup
Oil	1 tsp
Water	1½ cups
Curd/buttermilk	2 cups
Fresh coconut (grated)	1 tbsp
Coriander leaves (finely chopped)	1 tbsp
Mixed English vegetables (finely chopped)	1 cup or more
Salt	to taste
Seasoning:	
Oil	1 tsp
Bengal gram	½ tsp
Black gram	1 tsp
Mustard	½ tsp
Asafoetida	a pinch
Green chilli/red chilli	1 or 2
Curry leaves (finely chopped)	6–8
Onion (finely chopped, optional)	¼–½ tsp

Method

1. Roast vermicelli in oil, and then cook in boiling water.
2. Cook the vegetables in minimum water.
3. Season curd (thick or diluted) with black gram, Bengal gram, mustard, asafoetida, green chillies/red chillies, curry leaves and onions (optional).
4. Add coconut, coriander leaves, salt, cooked vermicelli, and cooked mixed vegetables and mix well.
5. Add grated cucumber and/or carrot ($\frac{1}{4}$ cup), optional. [Approx. **160 cal/serving**]

(iii) Vermicelli Upma (4 servings)

Ingredients	Quantity
Vermicelli	1 cup
Oil	1 tsp
Mixed English vegetables (finely cut)	2 cups
Salt	to taste
Water	$1\frac{1}{2}$ cup
Lime juice	to taste
Seasoning:	
Oil	1 tsp
Bengal gram	$\frac{1}{2}$ tsp
Black gram	1 tsp
Mustard	$\frac{1}{2}$ tsp
Green chilli (paste/pieces)	$\frac{1}{2}$ tsp
Ginger (paste/pieces)	$\frac{1}{2}$ tsp
Curry leaves	6–8
Onion (finely chopped, optional)	$\frac{1}{4}$ cup

Method

1. Cook the vegetables in minimum water.
2. Roast vermicelli in oil.
3. Add salt and water to the seasoning and boil.
4. Add roasted vermicelli and vegetables, mix well and cook on low fire till done.
5. Squeeze lime juice on upma. [Approx. **110 cal/serving**]

11

Soups

The following recipes will serve 6 people unless otherwise stated.

1. Bottle Gourd Soup (4 servings)

Ingredients	Quantity
Bottle gourd (unpeeled) (big pieces)	¼ kg
Onion (cut into quarters)	1 medium sized
Garlic	2 flakes
Peppercorns	2–3
Ginger	½" piece
Water	2½ cups
Salt	to taste
Milk	4 tbsp

Method

1. Pressure cook bottle gourd, onion, garlic, peppercorns and ginger with water.
2. Cool and strain.
3. Churn the boiled vegetables in mixie and then sieve.
4. Boil and add salt.
5. Add milk and serve hot. [Approx. 34 cal/serving]

2. Carrot Soup (4 servings)

Ingredients	Quantity
Carrot (big pieces)	¼ kg
Apple/potato	1 medium sized
Onion (cut into quarters)	1 medium sized
Garlic	2 to 3 flakes
Ginger	½" piece
Peppercorns	3

Ingredients	Quantity
Sugar	1 tsp
Water	2½ cups
Salt	to taste
Milk (optional)	4 tbsp

Method

1. Boil carrot, apple/potato, onion, garlic, ginger, peppercorns and sugar in water.
2. Churn the boiled vegetables in a mixie and then sieve.
3. Add salt and water, and boil once.
4. Add milk, and serve hot. [Approx. **68 cal/serving**]

3. Cauliflower Soup (6 servings)

Ingredients	Quantity
Cauliflower	¼ kg
Peppercorns	5
Onion (cut into quarters)	1 medium-sized
Bay leaves	1 or 2
Tomato (optional)	1 or 2 medium-sized
Water	5 cups
Milk	6 tbsp
Salt	to taste
coriander leaves (finely chopped)	1 tbsp

Method

1. Boil cauliflower with peppercorn, onion, bay leaves, and tomato, in water in a pressure pan.
2. Churn the boiled vegetables in a mixie and then sieve.
3. Add milk, and bring to a boil again.
4. Add salt, stir, sprinkle coriander leaves and serve hot. [Approx. **36 cal/serving**]

4. Chinese Mixed Vegetable Soup

Ingredients	Quantity
oil	1 tsp
Onion (finely chopped)	2 tsp
Garlic (finely chopped)	1 tsp

Ingredients	Quantity
Carrot (finely chopped)	¾ cup
Cabbage (finely chopped)	1 cup
Cauliflower (finely chopped)	½ cup
Celery/lettuce/spinach (finely chopped, optional)	½ cup
Mushroom	½ cup
Water	4 cups
Soya sauce	½ tsp
Chilli sauce (optional)	1 tsp
Vinegar	1 tsp
Pepper powder	½ tsp
Salt	to taste

Method

1. Heat oil in a non-stick pan, add onion, garlic, carrot, cabbage, cauliflower, celery, and mushroom and mix well.
2. Add water and boil.
3. Add soya sauce, chilli sauce, vinegar, pepper and salt, and boil once. Serve hot. [Approx. **17 cal/serving**]

5. Fresh Corn Soup

Ingredients	Quantity
Corn (grated/coarsely ground)	2 cups
Water	4 cups
Carrot (finely diced/grated)	½ cup
Cabbage (finely chopped/grated)	½ cup
Corn flour/whole wheat flour (optional)	2 tsp
Pepper powder	½ tsp
Salt	to taste
Chilli/tomato sauce	to taste
Vinegar (optional)	to taste

Method

1. Grate or coarsely grind fresh corn in a mixie.
2. Put water into a pan and boil corn for 10–15 minutes.
3. Blend the cooked corn in a mixie.

4. Pour into a pan and add carrot, cabbage, corn flour, pepper powder and salt.
5. Boil once. Serve hot with chilli/tomato sauce and vinegar. [Approx. **34 cal/serving**]

Note: If a thinner soup is desired, use more water.

6. Green Pea Pod Soup (4 servings)

Ingredients	Quantity
Cauliflower stems	2
Peeled pea pods (cellulose removed)	25–30
Onion (cut into quarters)	1 medium-size
Tomato (cut into quarters)	2 medium-size
Garlic	2–3 flakes
Ginger	½" piece
Peppercorns	8
Water	4 cups
Salt	to taste
Pepper powder	½ tsp
Milk	4–6 tbsp
Low fat cream (optional)	1 tsp

Method

1. Boil cauliflower stems, pea pods, onion, tomato, garlic, ginger, and pepper in water.
2. Blend in a mixie.
3. Strain through a fine sieve to remove any skin fibre.
4. Add salt, pepper powder and milk to the strained fluid.
5. Serve hot with low fat cream. [Approx. **30 cal/serving**]

7. Mixed Vegetable Soup (5 servings)

Ingredients	Quantity
Beans (2" pieces)	50 g
Spinach/goosefoot white (finely cut)	50 g
Turnip/radish (1" cubes)	50 g
Tinda/gourd (1" cubes)	50 g
Water	2½ cups

Ingredients	Quantity
Salt	to taste
Pepper powder	¼ tsp
Milk	5 tbsp

Method

1. Pressure cook the vegetables in water.
2. Cool and blend in a mixie.
3. Boil once and add salt, pepper powder and milk. Serve hot. [Approx. **28 cal/serving**]

8. Mushroom Soup (6 servings)

Ingredients	Quantity
Mushroom	200 g
Onion (cut into quarters)	1 medium-size
Garlic	2–3 flakes
Butter	1 tsp
Water	5 cups (total)
Pepper powder	¼ tsp
Salt	to taste
Milk	1 cup
Chilli sauce (optional)	to taste

Method

1. Heat butter in a pan.
2. Add mushroom, onion and garlic.
3. Stir on low fire for 2–3 minutes.
4. Blend in a mixie with one cup of water.
5. Pour into a pan add the rest of the water, pepper, salt and milk and boil.
6. Serve hot with chilli sauce. [Approx. **27 cal/serving**]

9. Parwal Soup (4 servings)

Ingredients	Quantity
Parwal (unpeeled)	200 g
Onion (cut into quarters)	1 medium-size
Ginger	½" piece

Ingredients	Quantity
Garlic	2–3 flakes
Peppercorns	5
Water	3½ cups
Salt	to taste
Milk	4 tbsp

Method

1. Pressure cook parwal, onion, ginger, garlic, pepper in water.
2. Blend the vegetables in a mixie and then sieve.
3. Add salt and milk. Serve hot. [Approx. **35 cal/serving**]

10. Pumpkin Soup (4 servings)

Ingredients	Quantity
Pumpkin (unpeeled with seeds) (2" cubes)	200 g
Onion (cut into quarters)	1 medium-size
Peppercorns	5–6
Water	3 cups
Salt	to taste
Milk	4 tbsp
Coriander leaves (finely chopped)	1 tbsp

Method

1. Boil pumpkin, onion, and peppercorns in water.
2. Blend the boiled vegetables in a mixie and then sieve.
3. Add salt and milk and boil once.
4. Garnish with coriander leaves and serve hot. [Approx. **36 cal/serving**]

11. Spinach Soup (4 servings)

Ingredients	Quantity
Spinach (finely chopped)	100 g
Potatoes (1" cubes)	1–2 medium sized
Onion (cut into quarters)	1 medium sized
Garlic	2–3 flakes

Ingredients	Quantity
Ginger	½" piece
Peppercorns	8
Cinnamon	½" piece
Water	2½ cups
Salt	to taste
Milk	1 cup

Method

1. Boil spinach, potatoes, onion, garlic, ginger, peppercorns, and cinnamon in water.
2. Blend the contents in a mixie and then sieve.
3. Add salt and milk.
4. Add more water if a thinner soup is required. Serve hot. [Approx. 57 **cal/serving**]

12. Tomato Soup (6 servings)

Ingredients	Quantity
Tomato (hybrid/normal) (cut into quarters)	½ kg
Carrot (1" pieces)	1
Apple/guava/potato (cut into quarters)	1 medium sized
Onion (cut into quarters)	1 or 2 medium sized
Garlic	2–3 flakes
Ginger	1½" piece
Peppercorns	8
Water	4 cups
Salt	to taste
Jaggery (bits and pieces)	½ tsp
Low calorie cream (optional)	1 tsp

Method

1. Pressure cook tomato, carrot, apple/guava/potato, onion, garlic, ginger, and peppercorns in water.
2. Add salt and jaggery, blend in a mixie and then sieve.
3. Serve hot with low calorie cream (optional).

4. If tomato is very sour, increase the quantity of water and potato. [Approx. **21 cal/serving**]

Note: Adjust the amounts of water and milk, in order to get the required consistency and taste. Add pieces of dry toasted whole wheat bread and low fat cream for extra flavour just before serving.

12

Salads

Salads are very good for health. They supply vitamins and minerals. Since the vegetables and fruit used are not cooked, their vitamin and mineral content remains intact. Salads should however be consumed as soon as they are prepared since, some vitamins and minerals are lost through oxidation.

In the following recipes, one serving consists of one bowlful of salad.

1. Cabbage-Carrot Salad (4 bowls)

Ingredients	Quantity
Cabbage (finely chopped)	2 cups
Carrot (finely grated)	1 cup
Tomato (finely chopped) (optional)	1 cup
Salt	to taste
Pepper powder	$1/4$–$1/2$ tsp
Lime juice	1 tsp

Method

Mix all the ingredients. [Approx. **26 cal/bowl**]

2. Cucumber-Coconut Salad ($2^1/2$ bowls)

Ingredients	Quantity
Cucumber (unpeeled) (finely diced)	2 cups
Fresh coconut (grated)	$1/2$ cup
Salt	to taste
Seasoning:	
Oil	$1/2$ tsp
Mustard	$1/2$ tsp

Ingredients	Quantity
Asafoetida	a pinch
Green chilli (pieces/paste)	1 tsp
Curry leaves	6–8

Method

1. Mix cucumber, coconut and salt.
2. Season with mustard, asafoetida, green chilli and curry leaves. [Approx. **52 cal/bowl**]

Note: Sprouted green gram (¼ cup) may also be added.

3. Cucumber Salad (3 bowls)

Ingredients	Quantity
Cucumber (unpeeled) (grated)	2 cups
Roasted groundnuts with skin (coarse powder)	¼ cup
Fresh coconut (grated)	¼ cup
Coriander leaves (finely chopped)	½ cup
Salt	to taste
Seasoning:	
Oil	½ tsp
Mustard	½ tsp
Cumin	½ tsp
Asafoetida	a pinch
Green chilli (chopped)	1 tsp
Curry leaves	6–8

Method

1. Mix cucumber, groundnut powder, coconut, coriander leaves and salt.
2. Add seasoning. [Approx. **73 cal/bowl**]

Note: Grated cucumber oozes water so the salad becomes a little watery. To avoid this, squeeze out the water from the cucumber (it can be drunk or added to any gravy). Alternatively, dice finely instead of grating it.

4. Green Sprout Salad (6½ bowls)

Ingredients	Quantity
Green gram/malki (sprouted)	2 cups
Groundnuts (sprouted)	½ cup
Fresh coconut (grated)	½ cup
Cucumber (unpeeled) (grated)	1 cup
Carrot (grated)	1 cup
Cabbage (grated)	½ cup
Coriander leaves (finely chopped)	½ cup
Green chilli (finely chopped/paste)	1 tbsp
Onion (finely chopped)	½ cup
Ginger (finely chopped)	1 tbsp
Lime juice	1 tbsp
Salt	to taste

Method

Mix all the ingredients together. [Approx. **68 cal/bowl**]

Note: Sprouted green gram and groundnuts can be steamed below 50°C in a pan for 2–3 minutes, though this entails some loss of nutrients.

5. Mixed Fruit and Vegetable Salad with White Sauce (7 bowls)

Ingredients	Quantity
Peas (fresh) (shelled)	½ cup
Potato (finely diced)	1 cup
Carrot (finely chopped/coarsely grated)	1 cup
Cabbage (grated)	1 cup
Apple (finely diced)	1 cup
Pineapple (finely diced)	1 cup
Orange (peeled and segmented)	1 cup
Salt	to taste
White sauce*	1½ cups

Method

1. Cook peas and potato in minimum water.

---

*The recipe for White Sauce is given on p. 284, under Some Basic Recipes.

2. Mix carrot, cabbage, apple, pineapple, orange, salt, white sauce,* with cooked peas and boiled potato. [Approx. 70 cal/bowl]

6. Mixed Vegetable Salad (5 bowls)

Ingredients	Quantity
Cucumber (unpeeled)	½ cup
Carrot	½ cup
Beetroot	¼ cup
Cabbage	¼ cup
Cauliflower	¼ cup
Radish	¼ cup
Fresh coconut (grated)	½ cup
Spring onions with bulbs (finely chopped)	½ cup
Tomato (finely chopped)	1 cup
Coriander leaves (finely chopped)	½ cup
Tender beans (finely chopped)	¼ cup
Green chilli paste	1 tsp
Jaggery (bits or pieces) (optional)	½ tsp
Salt	to taste
Lime juice to taste (optional)	

Method

1. Mix all the vegetables. Add coconut, green chilli paste, jaggery, salt and lime juice, and mix well. [Approx. 28 cal/bowl]

7. Mixed Vegetable Salad with Curd Dressing (4½ bowls)

Ingredients	Quantity
Cabbage (finely chopped)	1 cup
Cucumber (unpeeled) (finely diced)	1 cup
Carrot (grated)	1 cup
Beetroot (grated)	½ cup
Salt	to taste
Curd	1 cup

---

*The recipe for White Sauce is given on p. 284, under Some Basic Recipes.

Method

1. Mix cabbage, cucumber, carrot, beetroot and salt.
2. Pour curd dressing* over the mixed vegetables. Mix just before serving. [Approx. **45 cal/bowl**]

8. Radish Salad *(3½ bowls)*

Ingredients	Quantity
Radish (finely grated)	2 cups
Fresh coconut (grated)	½–1 cup
Fresh pomegranate seeds	½ cup
Salt	to taste

Method

Mix all the ingredients. [Approx. **28 cal/bowl**]

9. Stuffed Tomato Salad *(very low calorie)*

Ingredients	Quantity
Tomato	4–5
Fresh coconut (grated)	1 tbsp
Vegetables (finely chopped)	2 tbsp
Any chutney	to taste
Coriander leaves (finely chopped)	2 tbsp
Green chilli paste	to taste
Salt	to taste

Method

1. Choose firm, ripe tomatoes and scoop out the insides.
2. Mix the scooped-out portion with any fresh masala or chutney and coconut, vegetables (including spring onion or onion), coriander leaves, green chilli paste and salt.
3. Stuff the scooped-out tomatoes with this mixture.

---

*See recipe for curd dressing on p. 246.

13

Nutritious Chutneys

Chutneys make any dish more tasty, be it snacks, dosa, idli, vada, samosa or even a meal.

In most cases, these chutneys are themselves quite rich and are heavy on the digestive system since high calorie ingredients are used.

This chapter, contains recipes for a range of relatively low calorie chutneys, which are both nutritious and fibre-rich.

Jaggery to taste can be added to all the chutneys where tamarind or any other sour ingredient is used.

1. Bottle Gourd Chutney for Dosas and Idlis (Low Calorie, High Fibre)

Ingredients	Quantity
Bottle gourd (unpeeled) (1 cm cubes)	4 cups (½ kg)
Water	1 ½ cups
Bengal gram (oven fried or roasted) (powdered)	2 tbsp
Fresh coconut (grated)	1½ cup or less
Green chilli	to taste
Salt	to taste
Curd	2 tbsp
Seasoning:	
Oil	½ tsp
Mustard	½ tsp
Curry leaves	6–8
Asafoetida	a pinch

Method

1. Pressure cook bottle gourd in water.
2. Cool and add Bengal gram powder, coconut, green chilli, curd and salt and grind into a fine paste.

3. Add seasoning of mustard, curry leaves and asafoetida.
4. Use tender coconut kernel instead of mature coconut. [Approx. **360 cal (total)**]

2. Coconut Chutney

Ingredients	Quantity
Fresh coconut (grated or finely chopped)	1 cup
Oil	1 tsp
Black gram	1 tsp
Mustard	½ tsp
Fenugreek seed (optional)	¼ tsp
Asafoetida	a pinch
Red chilli	1–2
Curry leaves	2–4
Tamarind	¼ lime-size ball
Turmeric powder	a pinch
Salt	to taste

Method

1. Roast black gram, mustard, fenugreek seeds, asafoetida, red chillies and curry leaves in oil.
2. Pound them; add tamarind, turmeric powder and salt, and pound again.
3. Add coconut and grind coarse or fine. [Approx. **225 cal (total)**]

3. Carrot/Fresh Coconut Chutney

For carrot and/or fresh coconut chutney follow the same procedure as for coconut chutney. Instead of coconut, use a combination of carrot (grated, 1½ cups) and fresh coconut (grated) (⅓ cup). [Approx. **215 cal(total)**]

4. Coriander Leaf—Fresh Coconut Chutney for Idlis and Dosas (Low Calorie, Highly Nutritious) – with all raw ingredients

Ingredients	Quantity
Coriander leaves (finely chopped)	1½ cups
Curry leaves	10–12
Green chilli	to taste
fresh coconut (grated)	1 or 2 tbsp

Ingredients	Quantity
Salt	to taste
Cumin	½ tsp
Garlic	2–4 flakes
Ginger	¼" piece
Groundnuts with skin	10
Lime juice/green mango/Indian goosebery	to taste
Onion (finely chopped)	¼ cup
Water	½–1 cup or as per consistency desired
Cucumber (raw peels)/Potato or any vegetable peel (cooked) }	optional

Method

1. Grind all the ingredients with water into a fine paste and season with mustard (½ tsp) and curry leaves (2–3).
2. The amount of coconut can be increased to even one cup to offset the predominant flavour of coriander leaves. Alternatively, use fewer coriander leaves. [Approx. **200 cal (total)**]

5. Coriander Leaf Chutney

i. With Raw Leaves

Ingredients	Quantity
Coriander leaves (finely chopped)	1 cup
Salt	to taste
Green chilli	to taste
Lime juice	1 tbsp

Method

Grind all the ingredients together using very little water. [Approx. **42 cal (total)**]

Note: Season black gram (½ tsp) and mustard (¼ tsp) and/or a little fresh coconut in ½ tsp oil. Powder coarsely and add to the chutney.

ii. With Fried Leaves

Follow the recipe for tomato chutney but omit asafoetida and use tamarind (essential) instead. [Approx. **120 cal (total)**]

6. Cucumber Chutney

Follow the recipe for coconut chutney, but use cucumber instead of coconut and grind coarsely. [Approx. **150 cal (total)**]

7. Fresh Tender Tamarind/Tamarind Leaf Chutney

Ingredients	Quantity
Fresh tender (green) tamarind (1 cm pieces)	1 cup
Salt	to taste
Green chilli	2
Turmeric powder	a pinch
Mustard	1 tsp
Fenugreek seed	½ tsp
Red chilli	1–2
Asafoetida	a pinch
Coriander seed	1 tsp
Seasoning:	
Oil	1 tsp
Mustard	½ tsp
Asafoetida	a pinch
Red chilli	1–2
Curry leaves	6–8

Method

1. Chop the ends of fresh tender (green) tamarind removing the string (as for beans).
2. Cut into pieces and lightly pound to remove the seeds (if any).
3. Add salt, green chilli, and turmeric and pound well.
4. Roast mustard, fenugreek seed, red chilli, asafoetida and coriander seed and turmeric powder.
5. Add this to the pounded tamarind.
6. Season with mustard, asafoetida, red chilli and curry leaves.
   [Approx. **255 cal (total)**]

8. Indian Gooseberry Chutney

(A) Ingredients	Quantity
Indian gooseberry (1 cm cubes)	1 cup
For the powder	
Oil	½ tsp
Mustard	1 tsp
Fenugreek seed	½ tsp
Red chilli	1–2
Asafoetida	a pinch
Salt	to taste
Turmeric powder	a pinch

Method

1. Fry mustard, fenugreek seed, red chilli and asafoetida in oil.
2. Pound with salt and turmeric powder into a fine powder. Add Indian gooseberry and grind finely.

B) Ingredients	Quantity
Indian gooseberry (1 cm cubes)	1 cup
Oil	1 tsp
Black gram	2 tsp
Mustard	½ tsp
Asafoetida	a pinch
Red chilli	1–2
Curry leaves (optional)	2–4
Salt	to taste
Turmeric powder	a pinch

Method

1. Fry black gram in oil until it becomes light brown.
2. Add mustard, asafoetida, red chilli and curry leaves and fry.
3. Pound with salt and turmeric powder into a fine powder.
4. Add Indian gooseberry cubes and grind into a fine paste. [Approx. **145 cal (total)**]

9. Mint/Pudina Chutney

i. With Raw Leaves

Ingredients	Quantity
Mint leaves (finely chopped)	½ cup
Coriander leaves (finely chopped)	½ cup

Ingredients	Quantity
Indian gooseberry/raw mango/lime juice	to taste
Garlic	2–3 flakes
Green chilli	to taste
Tomato (cut into quaters)	1 medium-size
Onion (cut into quarters)	1 medium-size
Cumin	½ tsp
Ginger	½" piece
Jaggery	½ tsp
Salt	to taste

Method

Grind all the ingredients together. [Approx. **102 cal (total)**]

ii. With Fried Leaves

Ingredients	Quantity
Mint leaves (finely chopped)	2 cups
Tamarind/raw mango	¼ lime-sized ball
Oil	1 tsp
Turmeric powder	a pinch
Salt	to taste
Seasoning:	
Oil	1 tsp
Black gram	1 tbsp
Mustard	½ tsp
Green chilli	1

Method

1. Make a seasoning of black gram, mustard and green chilli.
2. Grind coarsely adding tamarind/raw mango.
3. Add mint leaves to hot oil in a pan and fry on low fire for a few minutes.
4. Add these leaves to the coarsely ground seasoning, turmeric powder and salt and grind into a paste. [Approx. **185 cal (total)**]

10. Pulse (Dal) Chutney

Ingredients	Quantity
Red gram/Bengal gram	1 cup

Ingredients	Quantity
Red chilli	2
Salt	to taste
Asafoetida	a pinch
Cumin	¼ tsp
Fresh coconut (grated) (optional)	to taste
Garlic flakes (optional)	to taste

Method

1. Dry roast red gram/Bengal gram and red chilli to redness on low fire.
2. Grind with salt, asafoetida, cumin and water into a coarse paste.
3. Fresh coconut can also be added and ground along with above ingredients.
4. Garlic flakes can be fried in a little oil and added towards the end of grinding or mixed as it is. [Approx. **375 cal (total)**]

11. Raw Mango-Fresh Coconut Chutney

Follow the recipe for coconut chutney but instead of tamarind, use raw mango (grated or finely cut, 1 cup or to taste). [Approx. **205 cal (total)**]

12. Raw Mango Chutney

Follow the recipe for Indian gooseberry chutney substituting gooseberry with raw mango. [Approx. **131 cal (total)**]

13. Ridge Gourd/Smooth Gourd Chutney

Follow the recipe for tomato chutney replacing tomato with gourd. [Approx. **140 cal (total)**]

14. Sprouted Pulse Chutneys (e.g. Green Gram, Matki, Bengal Gram)

Wash whole green gram, soak in water (for 18 hours in winter and 10–12 hours in summer keeping the pan covered) until the grain is well softened. Drain the water, but do not throw it away as it contains soluble nutrients. Use it for your cooking or drink it.)

Another method is to tie the soaked green gram in muslin or porous cloth and sprinkle water on the cloth every few hours (to keep it moist). The green gram will sprout. In winter it takes longer to soak and sprout. Once the green gram is sprouted and the sprout (radical) is about 2–3 mm long, it can be eaten raw as it is (ideal) or sprinkled with salt, lime juice and chilli powder. A salad or chutney can also be made with it. The chutney should be eaten as soon as it is prepared to avoid loss of nutrients by oxidation.

Sprouted Pulse Chutney

Ingredients	Quantity
Sprouted gram	1 cup
Salt	to taste
Green chilli	1
Coriander leaves (finely chopped)	½ cup
Indian gooseberry/raw mango/lime juice	½ slice/½ tsp
Cumin	¼ tsp
Fresh coconut (grated)	1–2 tbsp
Onion (finely chopped)	1 medium-size
Uncooked/cooked peels of vegetables	

Method

1. To the sprouted gram add salt, green chilli, coriander leaves (for flavour and taste), Indian gooseberry/raw mango/lime juice, cumin, coconut and onion, and grind coarsely.
2. The ingredients can be varied according to taste and availability.
3. Add the boiled peel of any vegetable while grinding, especially peel of potato and bottle gourd.
4. Cucumber peel, curry leaves and mint add taste and flavour to the chutney. [Approx. **200 cal (total)**]

Note: Small quantities of raw vegetables like carrot, cabbage, cauliflower, beans, tomato etc. can also be added to vary the taste.

15. Sweet Potato Chutney

Follow recipe for coconut chutney but use sweet potato instead of coconut. Add a little jaggery and coriander leaves while grinding. [Approx. **225 cal (total)**]

16. Tomato Chutney

Ingredients	Quantity
Oil	1 tsp
Tomato (finely chopped)	2 cups
Onion (finely chopped) (optional)	½–1 cup
Tamarind	to taste
Salt	to taste
Turmeric powder	a pinch
Seasoning:	
Black gram	1 tsp
Mustard	¼ tsp
Red chilli	1–2
Asafoetida	a pinch

Method

1. Add onion and tomato to hot oil, and cook till done.
2. Season black gram, mustard, red chillies and asafoetida and, coarsely grind with tamarind, salt and turmeric powder.
3. Add cooked tomato and onion. Grind into a paste.
4. A little jaggery can be added if desired. [Approx. **120 cal (total)**]

17. Vegetable Peel Chutney

Vegetable peel contains cellulose or roughage which is necessary for digestion and bowel movement. It acts like a broom for the intestines, enabling the quick removal of waste matter. [Moreover, the rays of the sun fall first on the peel and then penetrate into the vegetable. The valuable solar energy which aids in the synthesis of vitamins, minerals and other nutrients, is also stored in the peel.]

Vegetable peel can be used to make tasty and nutritious chutneys when combined with coconut and lime.

Ingredients	Quantity
Potato, bottle gourd/ridge gourd peel (finely chopped)	1 cup
Salt	to taste
Jaggery	¼ tsp (bits or pieces)
Turmeric powder	a pinch
Fresh coconut (grated)	1–2 tbsp

Ingredients	Quantity
Tamarind/lime/green mango/ Indian goosberry	to taste
Seasoning:	
Oil	1 tsp
Bengal gram (optional)	1 tsp
Black gram	1 tsp
Mustard	¼ tsp
Curry leaves	10
Asafoetida	a pinch
Green chilli	to taste

Method

1. Peel potatoes, bottle gourd/ridge gourd etc.
2. Cook the peel dry or in minimum water in pressure cooker or pan and drain the water if any.
3. Prepare the seasoning of bengal gram (optional), black gram, mustard, curry leaves, asafoetida and green chilli to taste.
4. Grind this coarsely, add the peel, salt, jaggery, turmeric powder, coconut, and tamarind/lime/greenmango/Indian gooseberry and grind again. [Approx. **225 cal (total)**]

Note: The uncooked cucumber peel can also be used for making chutney. The peel of fruit like pear, apple and guava can be added to the chutney while grinding.

14

Raitas and Dips

Curd for Raitas

a) With Seasoning

Ingredients	Quantity
Curd	2 cups
Salt	to taste
Turmeric powder	a pinch
coriander leaves (finely chopped)	1 tbsp
Fresh coconut (grated)	1 tbsp
Seasoning:	
Oil	1 tsp
Black gram	1 tsp
Mustard	$\frac{1}{2}$ tsp
Green/red chilli	1–2
Cumin	$\frac{1}{2}$ tsp
Asafoetida	a pinch
Curry leaves	6–8
Onion (finely chopped, optional)	$\frac{1}{4}$–$\frac{1}{2}$ cup

Method

1. Add salt, turmeric powder and the seasoning to curd.
2. Coriander leaves and coconut may also be added [Approx. 250 cal (total)]

b) Curd without Seasoning

Ingredients	Quantity
Curd	2 cups
Salt	to taste
Cumin (freshly roasted) (powdered)	$\frac{1}{2}$ tsp

Ingredients	Quantity
Red chilli powder	¼ tsp
Coriander leaves (finely chopped, optional)	1 tbsp

Method

Mix all the ingredients. [Approx. **145 cal (total)**]

I. Boiled Vegetable Raita

Ingredients	Quantity
Vegetables (finely chopped)	1 cup
Curd	2 cups

Method

Vegetables like potato, gourds (smooth, ridge and snake gourd), spinach, goosefoot white, boiled and partly mashed fresh corn, baked brinjal, potato and raw banana are most suitable for this type of raita. Boil or cook these vegetables and mix them with curd, with or without seasoning. [Approx. **67 cal/serving**]

2. Carrot–Cucumber Dip

Ingredients	Quantity
Curd	1½ cups
Salt	½ tsp
Sugar	1 tsp
Pepper powder	½ tsp
Cucumber (grated)	1 cup
Carrot (grated)	1 cup

Method

1. Tie curd in muslin or porous cloth for 1–2 hours.*
2. Blend the strained curd with salt, sugar and pepper powder.
3. Add cucumber and carrot. [Approx. **240 cal (total)**]

---

*The strained liquid is nutritious and should not be wasted. It may be drunk or used in gravy for kneading flours.

3. Onion–Garlic Dip

Ingredients	Quantity
Curd	1½ cups
Fresh garlic paste	½ to 1 tsp
Salt	½ tsp
Malt vinegar	1 tsp
Onion (finely chopped)	½ cup
Coriander leaves (finely chopped)	½ cup
Green chilli paste	½ tsp
Potato chips/chops/spinach gattas/pakoras	as required

Method

1. Tie curd in muslin or a porous cloth for 1–2 hours.
2. Blend curd with garlic, salt and malt vinegar.
3. Add onion, coriander leaves and green chilli paste.
4. Serve with potato chips, chops (p. 209), spinach gattas (p. 218) or pakoras. [Approx. **200 cal (total)**]

4. Raw Vegetable Raita (2 servings)

Ingredients	Quantity
Vegetable (finely diced/grated)	1 cup
Curd	2 cups

Method

Vegetables like cucumber, carrot, onion, tomato, radish, banana stem/pith and coconut are most suitable for this type of raita. These vegetables can be either finely cut or grated and then mixed with the curd. Season if necessary. [Approx. **67 cal/serving**]

15

Vegetable Pulaos and Vegetable Rice

In all the recipes for rice dishes (except pulaos) given below wherever cooked/pre-cooked rice is mentioned, the rice should be cooked with just enough water so that the grains remain separate.

1. Brinjal Rice (2 servings)

Ingredients		Quantity
Cooked rice		2 cups
Green chilli		4
Onion (finely chopped)		½ cup
Poppy seed		1 tbsp
Whole groundnuts with skin or cashew nuts (ground)		12 to 14
Fresh coconut (grated)	grind finely	½ cup
Tamarind		1 lime-sized ball
Turmeric powder		¼ tsp
Coriander leaves (finely chopped)		1 cup
Salt		to taste
Water		¼ cup
Brinjal (1–1½" slices)		4 cups
Onion (1–1½" slices)		½–¾ cup
Oil		2 tsp

Method

1. Grind green chilli, onion, poppy seed, groundnuts/cashew nuts, coconut, tamarind, turmeric powder, coriander leaves and salt into a thick fine paste.
2. Boil water in a *kadai*, add brinjal and cover with a lid on which water is poured.
3. Keep on high heat initially for a minute or two, then on low heat for 5 minutes.

4. Add salt and onion. When almost done, add the ground paste and mix and fry on low fire.
5. Do not cover the *kadai*; stir intermittently. Continue to cook till the smell of raw masala disappears and there is a pleasant aroma of fried masala.
6. Keep stirring so that the masala does not stick to the bottom of the pan.
7. Add oil, stir for a few minutes* then add the cooked rice and mix well. [Approx. **242 cal/serving**]

2. Curd Rice with Vegetable (3 servings)

See recipe for Beaten Rice Bhath (p. 191) Curd Bhath (p. 191) but substitute well- cooked and mashed rice for beaten rice to get the typical taste of south Indian curd rice.

or

To any vegetable raita (2 cups) described on pp. 246–48, add well-cooked and mashed rice (1 cup). Mix well. [Approx. **103 cal/serving**]

3. Fenugreek Leaf Rice (2 servings)

Ingredients	Quantity
Cooked rice	3 cups
Oil	1 tbsp
Fresh fenugreek leaves (finely chopped)	2 cups
Salt	to taste
Turmeric powder	a pinch
Thick tamarind extract (optional)	½–1 tbsp
For the powder:	
Oil	½ tsp
Coriander seed	2 tsp
Black gram	2 tsp

---

*Instead of frying in a *kadai* after adding the paste, frying on a *tava* is easier and faster. After the masala paste is added and mixed with the almost cooked brinjal, transfer to a hot greased *tava*. Keep on medium flame and when fried, turn the pieces of brinjal over and fry till the raw smell disappears.

Ingredients	Quantity
Red chilli	to taste
Fresh coconut (grated)	2 tbsp
Seasoning:	
Oil	1 tsp
Black gram	1 tsp
Mustard	½ tsp
Onion (finely chopped)	1 cup

Method

1. Roast black gram,* coriander seed, red chilli and coconut in oil.
2. Powder them.
3. To hot oil, add fenugreek leaves, salt, turmeric powder and cook on low fire.
4. Add cooked rice, black gram powder, tamarind pulp, more salt.
5. Season with black gram, mustard and onion. [Approx. **238 cal/serving**]

4. Mint Rice (3 servings)

Ingredients		Quantity
Cooked rice		2 cups
Fresh coconut (grated)		½ cup
Green chilli		1
Ginger grind	grind	1" piece
fresh mint leaves (finely chopped)		½–1 cup
Turmeric powder		a pinch
Seasoning:		
Oil		1 tsp
Cardamom		2
Cinnamon		1" piece
Cloves		2–3
Bay leaves		2
Onion (finely chopped)		½ cup
Vegetables like potatoes, green peas, beans, cabbage, cauliflower and carrot (finely diced)		2 cups
Lime Juice (optional)		

---

*Instead of 2 tsp each of coriander seed and black gram, for the powder 4 tsp black gram only can be used.

Method

1. Cook vegetables in minimum water or steam them.
2. Grind coconut, green chilli, ginger, mint leaves and turmeric powder into a paste.
3. Add seasoning of cardamom, cinnamon, cloves, bay leaves and onion.
4. Add cooked vegetables and cooked rice. Mix and remove from fire.
5. Squeeze lime juice over rice if desired. [Approx. **123 cal/serving**]

Note: The vegetables may be omitted altogether and only cooked rice (4 cups) used.

5. Pumpkin Pulao (3 servings)

Ingredients	Quantity
Pumpkin (grated)	1 cup
Rice	1 cup
Salt	to taste
Water	2 cups
Seasoning	
Oil	1 tsp
Peppercorns	6–8
Cinnamon	2" piece
Aniseed	1 tsp
Onion (finely chopped)	½ cup

Method

1. To the seasoning, add pumpkin, and washed and drained rice.
2. Fry a little, add salt and cook in water till done. [Approx. **182 cal/serving**]

6. Spinach Pulao (2 servings)

Ingredients		Quantity
Coriander leaves (finely cut)		2 tbsp
Green chilli (ground)	grind	1
Fresh coconut (grated)		1 tbsp
Ginger		1" piece

Ingredients	Quantity
Spinach (finely chopped)	2–3 cups
Green peas (shelled)	$\frac{1}{4}$–$\frac{1}{2}$ cup
Rice	1 cup
Salt	to taste
Water	2 cups
Seasoning:	
Oil	1 tbsp
Onion (finely chopped)	$\frac{1}{2}$–$\frac{3}{4}$ cup
Cumin	$\frac{1}{4}$ tsp

Method

1. Grind coriander leaves, green chilli, coconut and ginger together.
2. Put the seasoning paste, spinach, and fresh peas into a *kadai* and fry a little.
3. Add washed and drained rice, salt and water, and cook till done. [Approx. **195 cal/serving**]

7. Tomato Rice (2 servings)

Ingredients	Quantity
Cooked rice	2 cups
Oil	1 tsp
cinnamon	1" piece
Peppercorns	5–6
Ginger (finely chopped)	1 tsp
Garlic (finely chopped)	1 tsp
Green chilli (finely chopped)	1 tsp
Onion (finely chopped)	$\frac{1}{2}$ cup
Turmeric powder	$\frac{1}{4}$ tsp
Tomatoes (hybrid/normal) (finely chopped)	2 cups/1$\frac{1}{2}$ cups
Salt	to taste

Method

1. Fry cinnamon, pepper, ginger, garlic, green chilli, onion and turmeric powder in oil.
2. Add tomato, cover and cook on low fire without adding water.

3. When done, add salt and cooked rice, mix well and serve. [Approx. **237 cal/serving**]

8. Vegetable Khichdi (with rice/broken whole wheat) (8 servings)

This is a nutritious dish with the minimum ill- effects of high protein, fat or starch. The vegetables which can be used for this khichdi are bottle gourd and cabbage, alone or combined with ridge gourd.

Ingredients	Quantity
Bottle gourd/ridge gourd/cabbage (1 cm cubes)	8–10 cups
Rice	2 cups
Split green gram (with skin)	½ cup
Water	8–10 cups
Salt	to taste
Seasoning:	
Oil	1 tsp
Bengal gram	1 tsp
Black gram	1 tsp
Mustard	½ tsp
Asafoetida	a pinch
Curry leaves	20–25
Turmeric powder	¼ tsp
Onion (finely chopped)	1 cup
Green chilli (paste)	2 tsp
Ginger (paste) (optional)	½ tsp
Garlic (paste) (optional)	1 tsp

Method

1. Pressure cook unpeeled vegetables, washed rice, split green gram with skin and water for 3–5 minutes after the first whistle.
2. Add salt and seasoning.
3. When cold, khichdi tends to thicken. Add some more water to get the desired consistency. [Approx. **274 cal/serving**]

16

Recipes for Pulses (Whole/Split with Skin, Sprouted/Unsprouted)

Avoid using pulses without skin. Instead, use whole or split pulses with their skin intact as the skin provides roughage. Sprouted pulses are more nutritious than unsprouted ones. Whole pulses that can be used are green gram, Bengal gram, matki, lentil, peas and bean seeds.

1. Bengal Gram/Green Gram/Matki/Lentil/Peas/Bean Seeds with Ginger and Tomato (3 servings)

Ingredients	Quantity
Bengal gram/green gram/red gram/ matki/lentil/peas/bean seeds	1 cup
Water	1½–2 cups
Salt	to taste
Coriander leaves (finely chopped) (garnish)	1 tbsp
Seasoning:	
Oil	1 tsp
Cumin	¼ tsp
Mustard (optional)	¼ tsp
Ginger (paste/pieces)	¼ tsp
Green chilli (paste/pieces)	¼ tsp
Turmeric powder	a pinch
Red chilli powder	¼ tsp
Coriander seed powder	¼ tsp
Cumin powder	½ tsp
Curry leaves (optional)	6–8
Tomato (1 cm cubes)	½ cup

Method

1. Cook the Bengal gram/green gram in water. Set aside.
2. Add tomatoes to the seasoning.
3. Cook for a minute or two, and then add cooked pulses along with the water used for cooking them.
4. Boil once. Garnish with coriander leaves. [Approx. **173 cal/serving**]

2. Bengal Gram/Green Gram/Matki/Lentil/Peas/Bean Seeds with Onion–Garlic–Ginger and Tomato (3 servings)

Ingredients	Quantity
Bengal gram/green gram/matki/ lentil/peas/bean seeds	1 cup
Water	1½–2 cups
Coriander leaves (finely chopped) (garnish)	1 tbsp
Seasoning:	
Oil	1 tsp
Cumin	¼ tsp
Onion (grated)	1 tbsp or more
Garlic (paste)	¼–½ tsp
Ginger (paste)	¼ tsp
Green chilli (paste)	¼ tsp
Turmeric powder	a pinch
Red chilli powder	¼ tsp
Salt	to taste
Tomato (finely chopped)	¼ cup

Method

1. Cook the pulses in water and set aside.
2. Add cumin, onion, garlic, ginger, green chilli, turmeric, red chilli powder and salt to hot oil and fry till golden brown, stirring constantly.
3. Add tomato and cook till the tomato softens.
4. Add cooked pulses along with the water used for cooking and boil once.
5. Garnish with coriander leaves. [Approx. **177 cal/serving**]

Notes: a) Instead of onion paste, finely cut onion can be used. Ginger is optional. b) Powdered roasted coriander seed, cumin seed and garam masala can also be added.

Most suitable pulses: Almost all.

3. Sprouted Bengal Gram, Fresh Green Whole Bengal Gram with Coconut-Onion Paste (3 servings)

Ingredients		Quantity
Sprouted/unsprouted Bengal gram/ fresh green whole Bengal gram		1 cup
Water		1½ cups
Fresh coconut (grated)		1 tbsp
Onion (1 cm cubes)	ground into a	¼ cup
Green chilli	fine paste	1
Cumin		¼ tsp
Seasoning:		
Oil		½ tsp
Black gram		¼ tsp
Mustard		¼ tsp
Curry leaves		6–8

Method

1. Cook sprouted/unsprouted Bengal gram/fresh green whole Bengal gram water.
2. Add the paste made of coconut, onion, green chilli and cumin.
3. Season. [Approx. **188 cal/serving**]

4. Green Gram (Whole/Split with Skin) with Lime Juice and Asafoetida (3 servings)

Ingredients	Quantity
Green gram (whole/split with skin)	1 cup
Water	2 cups
Salt	to taste
Lime juice	1–2 tbsp
Seasoning:	
Oil	½ tsp
Mustard	¼ tsp

Ingredients	Quantity
Cumin	¼ tsp
Green chilli	2
Asafoetida	a pinch
Curry leaves	6–8
Turmeric powder (optional)	a pinch

Method

1. Cook green gram in water. Add salt and boil once.
2. Add lime juice to taste. Do not heat.
3. Season. [Approx. **166 cal/serving**]

5. Usal or Amti (with Whole and Preferably Sprouted Pulses) (4 servings)

See recipe for Green Peas Usal or Amti on p. 143. [Approx. **162 cal/serving**]

Most suitable dals: Green peas, whole pulses like matki, green gram and lentil.

17

Low-Calorie Jaggery Sweets

The recipes for the simple sweets given below are not for 'rich' sweets. They are for sweets that are relatively less concentrated and lower in calories than traditional, 'rich' sweets containing milk, maida, dals and ghee. Very little (if any) fat ghee/butter is used. Fresh coconut (with its fibre content, minerals, vitamins and fat in its colloidal, more easily digestible, form) is used in some of them. However, coconut need not be used. Jaggery is used in all the recipes as it is more nutritious than sugar which loses vitamins and minerals during its processing and therefore deflets our body of this. Whole ingredients with higher fibre content have been used.

If more tasty, 'richer' sweets are required: i) substitute milk or concentrated milk for water and increase the quantity of milk as desired. ii) use as much ghee/butter as needed iii) substitute sugar for jaggery and iv) use maida instead of whole wheat flour.

Choose jaggery which is free from sand/fine stones, bark and is not salty. If however, the jaggery looks impure add half a cup of water to the jaggery , heat on low fire till the jaggery melts, leave it undisturbed to cool, filter through a fine sieve or decant the clear jaggery water. Heat this till it thickens to the required consistency and then use.

1. Beaten Rice Payasam (Thick)

Ingredients	Quantity
Beaten rice	½ cup
Milk	1 cup or more
fresh coconut (grated)	½ cup
Jaggery (grated or fine powder)	1½ cups
Cardamom powder	to taste
Whole wheat flour biscuits/pieces of sweet brown bread (optional)	2
Dry fruit (chopped, optional)	to taste

Method

1. Add beaten rice to hot milk and cook adding more water or milk if need be till it thickens and becomes semi-solid.
2. Add coconut and jaggery and keep on low fire till the jaggery melts and the mixture thickens again.
3. Add cardamom powder and remove from fire.
4. Add crumbled whole wheat flour biscuits and/or pieces of sweet brown bread pieces and dry fruit. [Approx. 865 cal (total)]

2. Beetroot Laddus or Halwa

Ingredients	Quantity
Beetroot (finely grated)	1 cup
Butter or cream	1 tbsp
Milk	½ cup
Fresh coconut (grated) (if desired for dressing/decoration)	¼ cup or more
Jaggery (grated or fine powder)	¾ cup
Cardamom powder	a pinch
Dry fruit (chopped)	to taste

Method

1. Roast dry fruit in a little ghee. Cook beetroot on low fire in butter (or cream) and milk in a *kadai* covered with a lid on which water is poured.
2. When almost done, add coconut and jaggery.
3. Stir intermittently during the initial stages and continuously afterwards till it forms a mass and leaves the sides of the vessel.
4. Add cardamom powder and roasted dry fruit and mix well.
5. Cool and make into balls or serve as it is, as halwa. Decorate with fresh grated coconut. [Approx. **610 cal (total)**]

3. Bengal Gram/Green Gram Balls (Poornam)

Ingredients	Quantity
Bengal gram/green gram (split without skin)	1 cup
Water	1 ½ cups
Jaggery (grated or fine powder)	1½–1¾ cups
Cardamom powder	a pinch
Fresh coconut (grated)	½ cup

Method

1. Pressure cook the pulses in water. Drain excess water, if any.
2. Grind the drained pulses coarsely without adding any water.
3. Dissolve jaggery in 2 tbsp water on low fire and boil for a minute.
4. Add cardamom powder, coconut, the ground pulses, mix well and cook on medium fire (stirring continuously) till it is thick enough to form firm balls.
5. Pour onto a greased plate and cut into pieces or roll into even-sized balls. [Approx. 875 **cal** (**total**)]

4. Bobbatlu (Puran Poli)

1. Knead whole wheat flour as for sweet chapati (See recipe for Sweet chapati/ Gulachi poli in this chapter).
2. Use the stuffing described in the above recipe, instead of the stuffing of gulachi poli and proceed as given therein.

5. Boorlu (Flour-coated Sweet Bengal Gram/Green Gram Balls)

Ingredients	Quantity
Raw rice	¾ cup
Black gram	¼ cup
Water	1 cup

Method

1. Wash and soak raw rice and black gram.
2. Grind them into a fine paste with the water used for soaking.
3. Dip the poornam balls (see recipe 3 above) in this fresh unfermented batter and deep fry to golden brown in groundnut oil.
4. The flour coating can be made thicker or thinner by adjusting the consistency of the batter.

6. Bottle Gourd and/or Green Gram (Split, with Skin) Payasam (Kheer)

Ingredients	Quantity
Bottle gourd (grated)	1 cup
Split green gram with skin	1 cup

Ingredients	Quantity
Milk	1 cup or more
Water	1 cup
Jaggery (grated or fine powder)	1–2 cups
Cardamom powder	a pinch
Dry fruit (chopped)	to taste

Method

1. Roast dry fruit in a little ghee.
2. Cook bottle gourd and/or pulses in milk and water (1 cup, when only green gram is used) on low fire until thick.
3. Cool slightly (otherwise the milk will curdle) and add the required amount of jaggery (1 cup for bottle gourd and 1 cup for green gram), and cardamom powder and cook on low fire till the jaggery melts and blends.
4. Add more milk if necessary (especially for green gram payasam) and roasted dry fruit.
5. The bottle gourd or green gram can be cooked in a pressure cooker in milk alone or with milk and water. The milk may curdle or coagulate. However, this will still taste good. If this taste is not liked, boil the gourd or the green gram in minimum water, add milk and cook till as thick as required. Cool to room temperature and then add jaggery, roasted dry fruit and cardamom and mix well. [Approx. **630 cal (total)**]

7. Chalimidi

Ingredients	Quantity
Rice	1 cup
Water	2 cups
Jaggery (grated or fine powder)	1 cup
Ghee	1 tsp
Cardamom powder	a pinch
fresh/dry coconut (1 cm thin bits)	¼ cup or to taste

Method

1. Soak rice in water for an hour.
2. Drain and spread on a thick cloth for 10 minutes so that most of the water is absorbed.

3. Grind in a mixie to get a fine flour. Sieve this flour to remove any coarse grain.
4. Roast the bits of coconut in a little ghee.
5. Dissolve jaggery in 4 tbsp water on low flame. Continue heating on low flame till a little bit of it when dropped in cold water does not flow or mix with the water but remains separate as a firm ball.
6. Remove from fire and add ghee (optional), cardamom powder, roasted coconut, and rice flour, and mix well.
7. Cool to get a mass which can be broken by hand. [Approx. **1542 cal (total)**]

Note: Roasted sesame seed (¼ cup) may also be added.

8. China Grass (Agar Agar) Sweet

Ingredients	Quantity
Jaggery (grated or fine powder)	¾–1 cup
Water	6 tbsp
China grass (small bits or powder)	1 tsp.
Milk	1 cup

Method

1. Dissolve jaggery in the minimum quantity of lukewarm water.
2. Add china grass to milk and heat. Let the milk simmer till the china grass dissolves.
3. Remove from fire and cool. Add the dissolved jaggery and mix well.
4. Pour into container and after it comes to room temperature, cool in a refrigerator to set it well. [Approx. **560 cal (total)**]

Notes:
   i) Add cardamom powder for flavour.
   ii) Add cut fruits (banana and mango) when it is moderately cold as otherwise the Agar Agar will set.
   iii) Add the dissolved jaggery only when the boiled milk has cooled a little otherwise the jaggery will curdle the milk. If, however, the boiled milk cools to room temperature it will set and when the dissolved jaggery is added and mixed, it will

not set again properly. Hence both the dissolved jaggery and the milk (with china grass) must be moderately hot.

iv) If the milk still coagulates, churn when moderately hot (with a hand churner or in a food processor) to get a uniform texture like that of milk. Then allow it to set.

9. Coconut Barfi with Jaggery (Kobbari Nouzu)

Ingredients	Quantity
Fresh coconut (grated)	2 cups
Jaggery (grated or fine powder)	1 cup
Cardamom powder	a pinch
Bengal gram flour	½ tsp

Method

1. Mix coconut with jaggery and cook on low flame in a pan or thick-bottomed pot, stirring intermittently.
2. When it starts leaving the sides of the pan, comes together and is slightly thick, add cardamom powder and Bengal gram flour.
3. Mix well and pour onto a greased plate.
4. Cut into squares or roll into balls when cool. [Approx. 480 cal (total)]

Note: If the barfi is a little sticky, reheat it for a while. If it breaks up into a powder, add a little hot water to it and make it into balls. A little practice is required to arrive at the correct stage of cooking.

10. Eggless Cake with Jaggery, Oil and Whole Wheat Flour

Ingredients	Quantity
Jaggery (grated or fine powder)	1 cup
Sour curd	1 cup
Oil (unrefined groundnut oil)	½ cup
Vanilla essence	½ tsp
Baking powder	½ tsp
Cooking soda	1 tsp
Whole wheat flour	2 cups

Method

1. To sour curd, add oil and jaggery. Churn well to dissolve the jaggery completely. Add vanilla essence and mix.
2. Add baking powder and cooking soda to whole wheat flour and sieve three times to ensure that the baking powder, soda and flour are thoroughly and evenly mixed.
3. Add the sieved flour to the jaggery mixture adding, if necessary, a little curd or milk to get a thick dropping consistency.
4. Pour into a greased and flour-dusted baking tray.
5. Bake in a moderate oven (200–220°C) till baked. [Approx. **1300 cal (total)**]

Note: a) Instead of a combination of baking powder ($\frac{1}{2}$ tsp) and cooking soda (1 tsp) just cooking soda or baking powder ($1\frac{1}{2}$ tsp) can also be used. b) The jaggery used must be free from impurities and should be non-salty.

11. Green Gram Balls (Poli Poornam)

Ingredients	Quantity
Green gram (split without skin)	1 cup
Water	1 cup
Jaggery (grated or fine powder)	$1\frac{1}{2}$ cups
Cardamom powder	a pinch
Fresh coconut (grated)	$\frac{1}{2}$ cup

Method

1. Wash and soak green gram in water for an hour. Drain all the water and spread gram on a dry cloth for a few minutes to dry well. Grind coarsely without adding water.
2. Steam in idli plates for 5–7 minutes (Do not steam for a longer time or the cake will become hard and dry).
3. Remove, cool a little and crumble the steamed cake into a powder while still warm. Break up any hard lumps with the help of a food processor.
4. Dissolve jaggery in $\frac{1}{2}$ cup water on low fire, add cardamom powder, coconut, the above green gram powder and mix well.

5. Stir continuously on medium fire till the mixture is thick enough to form firm balls.
6. Make even-sized balls. [Approx. **900 cal (total)**]

12. Laddus with Beaten Rice (Laskora)

This is a sweet from rural Andhra Pradesh and has a unique rich taste.

Ingredients	Quantity
Beaten rice/unsalted puffed rice (coarse powder)	1–1½ cups
Fresh coconut (pieces/grated)	½ cup
Jaggery (grated or fine powder)	1½ cups
Cardamom powder	a pinch

Method

1. Pound by hand or grind in a mixie, beaten rice (preferably the hand-pounded variety) or unsalted puffed rice to reasonable coarseness.
2. Coarsely pound the pieces of coconut.
3. Add jaggery and pound again. The coconut and jaggery will form a sticky mixture.
4. To this, add cardamom powder and the beaten rice powder till it is possible to form balls of the mixture by hand.
5. Make even-sized balls. [Approx. **700 cal (total)**]

Note: i) If made with puffed rice, this sweet can be eaten immediately. ii) If made with beaten rice, it may be eaten after keeping for an hour or two to allow the beaten rice powder to soften. iii) The jaggery used must be free from impurities and should be non-salty.

13. Modaks

Ingredients	Quantity
Fresh coconut (grated)	1 cup
Jaggery (grated or fine powder)	½ to 1 cup
Cardamom powder	a pinch
Bengal gram flour	½ tsp
Water	¾ cup

Ingredients	Quantity
Rice flour	½ cup
Salt (optional)	a pinch

Method

1. Mix coconut with jaggery and cook on low fire in a *kadai* until the jaggery melts.
2. Continue to heat on medium fire until the mixture begins to froth, and comes together in a lump.
3. Stir intermittently.
4. Add cardamom powder and Bengal gram flour, mix thoroughly and remove from fire.
5. Boil water in a *kadai*, add rice flour, salt (optional) and mix well till the flour forms a dough. Remove from fire. Allow to cool.
6. Roll this into small balls.
7. Moisten the palm with a little water, place one small ball (of rice paste) on it, flatten a little to reasonable thinness with the other hand and place a teaspoon of the coconut-jaggery mixture in the centre.
8. Envelop it carefully with the remaining dough of the ball, wetting the hand with water or melted ghee.
9. Shape into balls or rolls.
10. Steam the balls (as for idlis) (for 5–10 minutes). [Approx. 375 cal (total) when ½ cup jaggery is used and 565 cal (total) when 1 cup jaggery is used]

14. Puffed Rice Balls

Ingredients	Quantity
Jaggery (grated or fine powder)	1 cup
Water	2 tbsp
Puffed rice	3–4 cups

Method

1. Dissolve jaggery in water by heating on low fire.
2. Continue heating till a drop of it when put in cold water

solidifies a little and does not flow or mix with the water but remains separate.

3. Immediately remove from fire, add the puffed rice and mix well.

4. Roll into balls when slightly cool greasing the palms with ghee (or spread on a greased plate). [Approx. **900 cal (total)**]

Note: The jaggery used should be free from impurities and salt.

15. Semolina Laddus (with/without Wheat Bran)

Ingredients	Quantity
Semolina	1 cup
Wheat bran (optional)	¼ cup
Fresh coconut (grated)	1 cup
Roasted groundnuts with skin (coarsely powdered)	½ cup
Cardamom powder	a pinch
Fresh dates (if available)	½ cup
Jaggery (grated or fine powder)	2 cups

Method

1. Dry roast semolina till the raw smell disappears.
2. Dry roast wheat bran until it becomes light pink or till roasted.
3. Add coconut, groundnut powder, cardamom powder and fresh dates, and mix.
4. Heat jaggery with a little (⅓ cup) water on low fire. When the jaggery melts, boil for about a minute.
5. Add the above mixture of rava and coconut to it and mix well. Remove from fire.
6. Cool till it is a just warm and then roll into balls, occasionally wetting the hands with a little water or ghee if needed.
7. If the laddu mix is a little thin, set it aside overnight and roll into balls the next day.
8. Keep for 2–4 days so that the suji and bran can soften in the jaggery. Serve thereafter. [Approx. **600 cal (total)**]

16. Rice Payasam (Kheer)

Ingredients	Quantity
Rice	1 cup
Water	1½ cups
Milk	1½ cups
Jaggery (grated or fine powder)	2 cups
Fresh coconut (grated)	1 cup
Cardamom powder	a pinch
Dry fruit	a few or to taste

Method

1. Roast dry fruit in a little ghee.
2. Pressure cook rice in milk and/or water (3 cups) to prevent the milk from curdling/coagulating. If cooked only in water, add milk (1½ cups or as required) and cook again till it thickens.
3. Add jaggery, coconut and cardamom powder and keep on fire for a minute or two till the jaggery melts and mixes uniformly.
4. Add roasted dry fruit. [Approx. **305 cal (total)**]

17. Sweet Boondi/Sev/Diamond Cuts made of Whole Wheat Flour

Ingredients	Quantity
Bengal gram flour/whole wheat flour	1 cup
Jaggery (grated or fine powder)	1 cup
Cardamom powder	a pinch

Method

1. Make the boondi or sev or diamond cuts bland without adding salt or masalas. For 1 cup flour used, take 1 cup of jaggery (fine pieces or grated) and add 2 tbsp water.
2. Keep on low fire till jaggery melts. Remove from fire.
3. Add cardamom powder and boondi, sev or diamond cuts.
4. Mix thoroughly and allow to cool, mixing intermittently so that jaggery covers the pieces uniformly. As the syrup cools, the jaggery will solidify, coating all the pieces uniformly. [Approx. **720 cal (total)**]

18. Sweet Chapati (Gulachi Poli)

Ingredients	Quantity
Whole wheat flour	3 cups
Oil	2 tbsp
Salt (optional)	a pinch
Ghee	1 tsp or more
Water	as needed

For the Stuffing:	
Ghee	½ tsp
Jaggery (grated)	3 cups
Poppy seed powder	3 tbsp
Sesame seed powder	3 tbsp
Dry coconut (powder)	2 tbsp
Oven-fried/roasted Bengal gram powder	2 tbsp
Cardamom powder	a pinch

Method for the Dough

1. Mix the flour thoroughly with oil, salt, (optional) and ghee.
2. Add about 1 cup water and knead into a soft dough. Set aside for ½ hour.

Method for the Stuffing/Filling

1. Separately roast poppy seed and sesame seed.
2. Powder them separately to get 3 tbsp powder of each.
3. Mix thoroughly a little ghee, jaggery, powdered poppy and sesame seed, dry coconut, Bengal gram powder and cardamom powder.

Chapati

1. Divide the kneaded flour into 32 even-sized balls.
2. Roll out one small chapati with one ball of the kneaded flour, put 1 tbsp (heaped) of the stuffing on this chapati and place another chapati of the same size on top of it.
3. Seal the ends by pressing them well with the hands (otherwise the melted jaggery will ooze out and char when the chapati is being roasted).
4. Sprinkle rice flour/wheat flour on and below the stuffed

chapati. Roll it lightly with a rolling pin without applying much pressure.

5. Roast the stuffed chapati carefully on medium or low fire on a *tava*, either with or without ghee. Serve hot. [Approx. **2380 cal (total)**]

An alternative stuffing/filling consists of ½ cup roasted sesame seed powder and ½ cup roasted groundnut (with skin) powder and 1 cup powdered jaggery.

19. Sweet Dosas

Ingredients	Quantity
Jaggery (grated or fine powder)	1 cup
Water	1 cup
Rice flour	1 cup
Whole wheat flour	1 cup
Fresh coconut (grated)	½ cup
Cardamom powder	a pinch
Cinnamon powder (optional)	a pinch
Oil	as required

Method

1. Dissolve jaggery in water.
2. Add flour, coconut, cardamom and cinnamon powder, and mix into dosa batter consistency.
3. Pour a ladleful of this batter on a hot thick bottomed *tava* and spread carefully to 4"–6" diameter.
4. Pour a little oil on the sides and bake on low heat.
5. When done, turn carefully as the dosas are sticky due to the melted jaggery. Serve hot. [Approx. **1150 cal (total)**]

20. Sweet Rice with Green Gram and Coconut (Chakkera Pongali)

Ingredients	Quantity
Rice	2 cups
Split green gram without skin	¾ cup
Milk	2½ cups
Water	2½ cups
Jaggery (grated or fine powder)	4 cups

Ingredients	Quantity
Fresh coconut (grated)	¾ cup
Cardamom powder	a pinch
Dry fruit (small pieces)	to taste
Bottle gourd (grated)	1 cup

Method

1. Roast dry fruit in a little ghee.
2. Dry roast green gram to a very light pink colour.
3. Pressure cook rice and green gram together in 2½ cups milk and 2½ cups water.
4. Add jaggery, coconut and 1 cup or more water or milk (as per the consistency desired), and cardamom powder.
5. Mix and keep on medium fire for a few minutes till well blended and a little thick.
6. Add the roasted dry fruit.
7. To add fibre content, cook 1 cup grated bottle gourd along with rice and green gram. Alternatively, add cooked bottlegourd to cooked rice and green gram. Increase the amount of jaggery accordingly. [Approx. **2700 cal (total)**]

21. Trifle Pudding with Jaggery and Eggless Cake

Ingredients	Quantity
Milk	2 cups
Sweet fruit (papaya, mango, chikkoo, fully-ripe bananas) (finely diced)	5 cups
Cream (optional)	1 tbsp
Jaggery (grated or fine powder)	1–1½ cups
Eggless cake (1 cm cubes)[*]	1 cup
Custard (1 cm cubes)	½ cup
Jelly (1 cm cubes)	½ cup

Method

1. Make eggless cake, custard and jelly to get the quantities given above.
2. Add the sweet fruit, cream and jaggery to the milk. Set aside for a while.

---

[*]Preparation of Eggless Cake, see page no. 264.

3. Mash a little so that the fruit and jaggery blend well with the milk.

4. Add eggless cake, custard, jelly and mix well. [Approx. **1370 cal (total)**]

Note: Instead of jelly, China grass (agar agar) sweet (see recipe 8 on p. 263) made with jaggery may be added. Custard has to be made with sugar since it does not taste good when made with jaggery. However, custard can be replaced with whole wheat flour biscuits or mashed rice or kheer (payasam). Whole wheat flour bread can also be added.

22. Vermicelli Payasam

Ingredients	Quantity
Sago pearls	1/4 cup
Water	1 1/2 cups
Vermicelli	1/2 cup
Ghee/butter/cream	1 tsp
Milk	2 cups
Jaggery (grated or fine powder)	1 cup
Cardamom powder	a pinch
Dry fruit	to taste
Bottle gourd (grated)	optional

Method

1. Roast dry fruit in a little ghee.
2. Soak sago pearls in water for 2–3 hours.
3. Roast vermicelli in ghee.
4. Cook soaked sago pearls in 2 cups milk and 1 cup water on low fire or in a pressure cooker.
5. When cooked add vermicelli and cook till desired consistency is reached.
6. Cool a little and then add jaggery, cardamom powder and keep mixing till jaggery dissolves.
7. Add roasted dry fruit.
8. If using bottle gourd, cook 1 cup grated bottle gourd in the minimum amount of water/milk and add it to payasam. Increase the amount of jaggery accordingly.

9. When cold, the payasam may thicken. Add milk or water to give it the desired consistency. [Approx. **810 cal (total)**]

23. *Well-ripened Banana Sweet*

Ingredients	Quantity
Milk	2 cups
Cardamom powder	a pinch
Jaggery (grated or fine powder)	½ cup or to taste
Well-ripened banana (mashed)	2 cups

Method

1. Add cardamom powder and jaggery to milk.
2. Set aside for 5–10 minutes so that jaggery softens.
3. Mix well till jaggery dissolves completely, add mashed banana and mix again.
4. The quantity of mashed banana can be increased to 4 cups if desired [Approx. **420 cal (total)**]

24. *Whole Wheat Halwa without Ghee*

Ingredients	Quantity
Whole wheat	1 cup
Water	2 cups
Jaggery (grated or fine powder)	1¼–1½ cups
Cardamom powder	a pinch
Dry fruit	to taste
Ghee	½–1 tsp

Method

1. Soak whole wheat in water for a day. Drain and use the water for gravies, kadis, or kneading dough, as this water contains the soluble nutrients of wheat.
2. Again add water to the drained wheat and leave for one day more or as required till the grain softens.
3. Coarsely grind in a mixie along with the water in which it was soaked till the grain is ground but not the skin.
4. Filter through a very fine double meshed filter or a fine thin cloth to get a milky liquid free from wheat fibre (skin) (first milk).

5. Add water again to the skin, mix well and again filter to get some more milky liquid (second milk). Use the skin residue to make dosas as discussed on page 203(vii).

6. Combine the first and second milk. Allow the milk to settle down by keeping it undisturbed for an hour or two in a rimmed pan in refrigerator in order to avoid fermentation. Decant the supernatant water very carefully so that the thick white milk remains behind. Set this aside for making the halwa.

7. Roast dry fruit in a little ghee.

8. Add ¼ cup water to jaggery, keep on low fire till jaggery dissolves and syrup thickens a little.

9. Add the above thick milk and stir continuously on low fire till the mixture thickness to form a mass, and it changes colour and no milk remains.

10. Add cardamom powder, roasted dried fruit and ghee. Mix well and remove from fire.

11. Spread this halwa on a plate greased with ghee and cut into squares when it cools. [Approx. **1886 cal (total)**]

25. Whole Wheat Rava/Semolina Halwa

Ingredients	Quantity
Milk	1 cup
Water	1 cup
Whole wheat rava/semolina	1 cup
Ghee or butter	1–2 tsp
Jaggery (grated or fine powder)	1½ cups
Fresh coconut (grated) (optional)	½ cup
Cardamom powder	a pinch
Dry fruit	to taste

Method

1. Roast dry fruit in a little ghee.
2. Roast whole wheat rava/semolina in ghee till it turns light pink.
3. Dilute milk with water and boil in a pan or *kadai*.

4. Add the roasted whole wheat rava/semolina, mix well to prevent lumps and cover the pan or *kadai* with a lid.
5. Let it cook on a low fire for a few minutes, then remove the lid and add jaggery powder.
6. Mix well and keep on low fire till it thickens, stirring constantly and mashing any lumps that may form.
7. Add coconut, cardamom powder and roasted dry fruit.
8. Mix well and remove from fire.
9. When cold, the halwa tends to thicken. Add a little milk or water to get the desired consistency. [Approx. **900 cal (total)**]

18

Masalas

1. Bisibela Powder

Ingredients	Quantity
Coriander seed	3 cups
Bengal gram (split)	1 tbsp
Black gram (split)	1 tbsp
Red chilli	to taste
Cinnamon	2"–3" piece
Fenugreek seed	½ tbsp
Dry coconut (grated)	1 cup
Cloves	½ tbsp
Cardamom	6
Poppy seed	1 tbsp
Nutmeg	small piece

Method

Fry all the ingredients in a little oil and then powder.

2. Curry/Dal Powder

i. With High Fibre

Ingredients	Quantity
Coriander seed	1 cup
Black gram	¼ cup
Red chilli	¼ cup
Bengal gram	½ cup
Asafoetida	a pinch
Pumpkin seed (sun-dried)	½ cup
Groundnut skin	1 tbsp (optional)

278 | *High Fibre, Low Calorie*

Method

Fry ingredients in very little oil and grind into a fine powder.

ii. Traditional Andhra Powder

Ingredients	Quantity
Black gram	¼ cup
Bengal gram	½ cup
Red chilli	to taste
Coriander seed (optional)	1 tsp
Cumin	1 tsp
Asafoetida	¼ tsp

Method

Fry until light red in 2 tsp of oil and powder coarsely.

3. Fenugreek–Mustard Seed Powder (Pulusu Powder)

Ingredients	Quantity
Fenugreek seed	1 tsp
Mustard	2 tsp
Asafoetida	a pinch
Red chilli	to taste

Method

Dry roast the ingredients to redness in a little oil and grind into a fine powder.

4. Garam Masala

Ingredients	Quantity
Coriander seed	1 cup
Cloves	1 cup
Cinnamon	1 cup
Cardamom	1 cup
Cumin seed	1 tsp

Method

Powder all ingredients together (no roasting or frying needed).

5. Iyengar Pulihodarai

Ingredients	Quantity
Coriander seed	1 cup
Sesame seed	2 cups
Red chilli	1 tsp
Cumin	1 tsp

Method

Fry all the ingredients in a little oil and then powder.

6. Maharashtrian Kala Masala Powder

Ingredients	Quantity
Coriander seed	8 cups
Cumin	¾ cup
Red chilli	¾ cup
Fenugreek seed	½ cup
Turmeric powder	2 tbsps
Cinnamon	½ cup
Peppercorns	¼ cup
Cloves	¼ cup
Asafoetida	2 big lumps
Black cumin (optional)	4 tbsp
Bay leaves (optional)	7–8
Dry coconut	2 cups
Sesame seed	1½ cups
Poppy seed	3–4 tbsp

Method

Fry each ingredient separately in a little oil and finely powder all the ingredients except the last three which have to be pounded (lightly but finely) separately and later mixed with the others, as they give out oil when pounded too vigorously. This oil will prevent the other ingredients from being finely powdered.

7. Panch Phoran

Ingredients	Quantity
Cumin seed (jeera)	1 cup
Aniseed	1 cup

Ingredients	Quantity
Onion seed	1 cup
Fenugreek seed	1 cup
Mustard seed	1 cup
Red chilli (whole)	1 cup

Method

Mix all the ingredients and use. There is no need to powder them.

8. Rasam or Sambar Powder

	Ingredients	Quantity
i.	**Coriander seed**	1 cup
	Red gram	⅓ cup
	Bengal gram	⅓ cup
	Cumin	1 tsp
	Fenugreek seed	2 tsp
	Peppercorns	1 tsp
	Turmeric powder	¼ tsp
	Red chilli	to taste
	Asafoetida	a pinch

or

	Ingredients	Quantity
ii.	**Coriander seed**	6 cups
	Bengal gram (split)	1 cup
	Cinnamon	1 piece
	Fenugreek seed	½–1 cup
	Red chilli	1 cup or to taste
	Asafoetida	a pinch

Method

Lightly roast the ingredients in a little oil or dry them in the sun for 1–2 days. Powder them finely (preferably in a mill).

	Ingredients	Quantity
iii.	**Only for sambar**	
	Coriander seed	2 cups
	Fenugreek seed	1 tbsp
	Red chilli	to taste
	Asafoetida	a small lump

Method

Fry the ingredients to mild redness in 1–2 tsp oil and powder them finely. When making sambar, take the required quantity (say 2 tsp for 1 cup of cooked dal) of the above powder, add fresh grated coconut (2 tbsp) and grind into a very fine paste with a little water so as to get a butter-like texture.

Measurement and Abbreviations

tsp =	teaspoon	1 tsp =	5 ml
tbsp =	tablespoon	1 tbsp =	3 tsp = 15 ml
1 cup =	180 ml = 1 bowl		
g =	gram	1 g =	1 ml water
mg =	milligram		
1" =	2.5 cms		
l =	litre	1 l =	1000 ml
kg =	kilogram	1 kg =	1000 g
cal =	calorie		
kcal =	kilocalorie		
1 bowl =	180 ml		

Glossary of Culinary Terms and Some Basic Recipes

Black gram =	split black gram with skin
Blend =	to combine and then mix to get a smooth and uniform mixture
Chop =	to cut very finely
Essence =	an extract or concentrate obtained from a particular plant or other matter and used for flavouring/scent e.g. vanilla essence
Frying pan/*tava* =	a concave or flat iron pan usually used for making chapatis/phulkas.
Garnish =	to decorate
Grate =	to cut finely using a grater.
Gravy/Rasa =	thick sauce that is part of a vegetable dish
Green chilli paste =	Pound green chillies with salt into a paste. *Note*: This can be made in bulk and preserved in a refrigerator for 10–15 days for ready use.
Oil used =	unrefined groundnut or til or sunflower oil
Pound or grind =	reduce to fine particles or to a pulp in a mixie or in a mortar
Seasoning =	Heat 1 tsp or ½ tsp oil in a *kadai* and add specified ingredient
Shred =	to cut very thin and long pieces especially of cabbage and onion
Slurry =	Flour (any) mixed with water to form a suspension in water. It is used to thicken a gravy.
Stock =	the liquid portion of boiled vegetables
Strain =	to pass through a sieve or muslin/porous cloth
Syrup =	a thick sweet liquid made by dissolving sugar jaggery in boiling water

Tamarind extract =   Soak washed tamarind in enough water to soften. Mash by hand and squeeze out the thick juice and pulp, discarding the seeds and bark, if any.

Note: Tamarind extract can be made in bulk and preserved in a refrigerator as follows using either of the methods given below

i. Wash tamarind (200 g) and add enough water to submerge it. Pressure cook and remove the skin, bark and string. Add salt (about 50 g), turmeric powder (1 tsp) and grind into a fine paste.

ii. Wash tamarind (200 g) and soak in enough water to submerge it. Let it soak for 2–3 hours. Squeeze out the water from the soaked tamarind by hand and filter tamarind through a sieve. Add some fresh lukewarm water and filter a second time. Repeat this process until only the seed, bark, string and skin are left over. Combine all three extracts. Add 50 g salt, 1 tsp turmeric and evaporate in a *kadai* on medium fire to a reasonably thick pouring consistency. Cool and then store in a refrigerator for ready use.

This extract can be added to any steamed/boiled vegetable. Since it is already cooked, it is not necessary to cook it again with the vegetable.

SOME BASIC RECIPES

1. White Sauce

Ingredients	Quantity
Corn flour/whole wheat flour	1 tbsp
Milk	1 cup
Malt vinegar	2 tsp
Oil	1 tsp
Pepper powder	$\frac{1}{4}$ tsp
Mustard powder	$\frac{1}{4}$ tsp
Sugar	1 tsp
Salt	to taste

Method

1. Make a slurry of flour in milk and boil till it thickness. Let it to cool.
2. Mix malt vinegar and oil in a mixie.
3. Add pepper powder, mustard powder, sugar, salt and the above cooked slurry.
4. Blend in mixie for a few minutes till it becomes a smooth paste.

2. Green chilli sauce

Ingredients	Quantity
Oil	1 tsp
Garlic (finely chopped)	2 tsp
Green chilli (finely chopped/sliced)	1 cup
Vinegar	1 tbsp
Salt	to taste

Method

1. Heat oil, add garlic and green chilli and saute for 2–3 minutes.
2. Add vinegar and salt to taste.
3. Cool and churn in mixie into a fine paste.
4. This sauce can be stored in a refrigerator for 2–3 months.

3. Curd Dressing

Ingredients	Quantity
Curd	1½ cups
Salt	½ tsp
Pepper powder	½ tsp
Sugar	1 tsp

Method

1. Tie curd in muslin or porous cloth for an hour.
2. Thoroughly blend the strained curd with salt, pepper powder and sugar, using a spoon.

NAMES AND LANGUAGES CHART

Common Name	Bengali	Gujarati	Hindi	Kannada	Kashmiri	Malayalam	Marathi	Oriya	Tamil	Telugu
Ash Gourd / Ash Pumpkin / Wax Gourd	Chaal Kumra	Kolo Bhuru Kohlu (Kohoro)	Petha	Budagum balakai	Mashaalyal	Elavan kumbalan-ga	Kohala (Pandhra Bopla)	Panikak-haru	Pushnikai	Budeda gummidi-kai
Asafoetida	Hing	Hing	Hing	Hingu (Ingu)	Yangu	Perunga-yam	Hing	Hingu	Peringayam	Inguva
Aniseed (fennel) (saunf)	Mourie	Saunf	Saunf	Badesepu	Saunf	Perinjeera-kam	Badishep	Paan mahuri	Shombu	
Amaranth (choulai)	Natya (Katoa)		Choulai saag	Dantu		Cheera	Choulai chi bhaji (math)	Kharada saag	Thandu keerai	Thotakura
Almond	Badam	Badam	Badam	Badam	Badam	Vatamkot-tai	Badam	Badam	Vadamkot-tai	Badamulu
Alfa-alfa	Brown seeds resembling black Til, rich in vitamins, minerals (and fibre) especially when sprouted.									
Apple	Seb	Safarjan	Seb	Sebu	Tsoonth		Safarchand	Sevuu	Apple	Apple
Apricot	Khobani		Khoomani	Sakkera badami	Tser					

NAMES AND LANGUAGES CHART

Common Name	Bengali	Gujarati	Hindi	Kannada	Kashmiri	Malayalam	Marathi	Oriya	Tamil	Telugu
Amchur/ dried mango powder	Amrochur-na	Amchur	Amchur or ambchur	Maavin kai podi	Amchur	Urianzha Mangapodi	Kache ambechi peeth	Ambala	Pache manga podi	Pachi mamidikai podemu
Agar Agar (China grass)	Falooda									Junnu gaddi
Ajwain	— See Thyme									
Amla	— See Indian Gooseberry									
Bengal gram / chick pea (whole)	Chola (gota) (Banglar chola)	Chana	Chana (Kala, sabut)	Kadale	Chanu	Kadala	Harbare	Buta	Kothukadalai / Muzukothu kadalai	Senagalu
Bengal gram (split)	Cholar dal	Chana dal	Chane ki dal	Kadale bele	Chola dal	Kadala parippu	Harbara (chanechi) dal	Chanyochi dal	Kadalai parappu	Senaga-pappu
Bengal gram (flour)	— See Besan									
Black gram (split)	Mashkalair dal	Urad dal	Urad dal	Uddina bela	Maha	Uzhunna parippu	Uddachi dal	Biri	Ultham parippu	Minappappu

288

NAMES AND LANGUAGES CHART

Common Name	Bengali	Gujarati	Hindi	Kannada	Kashmiri	Malayalam	Marathi	Oriya	Tamil	Telugu
Banana / plantain stem (pith)	Thor	Kelanu thed	Keleka ka danda (thane)	Dindu		Vazhap-pindi (unnipindi)	Kelicha khunt	Kadali manja	Vazhai thandu	Aratiduvva (Aratidoota)
Black cumin seed	Kalojeera (kalo jirra)	Shahjira	Shahjira	Kappu jeerige			Shahjeera	Shahjeera	Karun jeeragam	Nalla sanna jeelakarra
Butter	Makhon	Makhan	Makhan	Benne	Thany	Venne	Loni	Loni	Vennai	Venna
Buttermilk	Donier ghol	Chaas	Lassi	Majjige	Chuaku duod	Moru	Taak	Ghola dohi	Mohr (moru)	Majjiga
Bay leaf (cassia leaf)	Tej patta	Tej patta	Tej patta	Biryani elai	Tejpatta	Vayne illa	Tej patta	Tej patta	Biryani elai	Biryani aku
Black pepper	— See pepper (peppercorn)									
Barley	Job	Jau	Jau	Jave godhi	Wushku	Yavam	Jau (Jav)	Jaba dhana	Barli arisi	Barli (biyyam)
Beetroot	Beet	Beet	Chukandar	Beet		Beetroot	Beet	Bita	Beet	Beet
Bitter gourd	Karela (Karola)	Karela	Karela	Hagalakai	Karela	Kaipakku/pavakka	Karle	Kalara	Pavakkai	Kakarakai
Bottle gourd	Lau	Dudhi	Lauki (ghiya)	Sorekai	Duagu'ral (zeeth)	Charanga/churakai	Pandhra bhopla / dudhi	Lau	Suraikai	Sorakai / anapakai

NAMES AND LANGUAGES CHART

Common Name	Bengali	Gujarati	Hindi	Kannada	Kashmiri	Malayalam	Marathi	Oriya	Tamil	Telugu
Brinjal (eggplant)	Begun	Ringan (ringna)	Baingan	Badane kai	Waangun	Vazhu thiringu	Wangi	Baigan	Kathirikai	Vankaya
Boiled rice /par boiled rice	Sheddho chowl	Ukadello chokha	Usna chawal	Kusubal akki		Puzhangal arisi	Ukda tandul	Usuna chaula	Puzhungal arisi	Uppudu biyyam
Beaten rice/ flattened rice/parched rice/rice flakes	Chira (chaler khood) (chidi)	Pohe	Chiwra	Avalakki		Aval	Pohe	Chuda	Aval	Atukulu
Bran (rice /wheat)	Bhunshi / goova tunsh	Thulu		Thevudu	Kosh	Thavudu	Konda	Boosa	Thavudu (Arisi / godhume)	Thavudu (Biyyam / godhuma)
Broad beans	Shim	Fafda papdi	Bakla sem	Chappara davare	Broad beans	Avrakka	Walpapdi	Simba	Avarakai	Pedda (vedalpu) chikkudu
Bajra	Bajra	Bajri	Bajra	Sajje	Bajru	Kambu	Bajri	Bajra	Kambu	Sajjalu (gantelu)
Basil	Tulshi	Tulsi	Tulsi	Tulsi	Tulsi	Tulasi	Tulsi	Tullasi	Tulasi	Tulasi

290

NAMES AND LANGUAGES CHART

Common Name	Bengali	Gujarati	Hindi	Kannada	Kashmiri	Malayalam	Marathi	Oriya	Tamil	Telugu
Bael/Bilwa fruit or leaves	Bel	Bil	Bel	Bipatre	Belpat	Bilwa pazham	Bel	Belo	Bilwa pazham	Maredu pandu/akul
Black salt	Kalo labon	Sanchal nu bhuko	Kala namak		Kuhoon noon	Enthupp	Kala meeth	Kala luna	Karuppu uppu	Nalla uppu
Bread (white)	Roti	Bread	Double roti	Bread	Chot	Bread	Pav	Pav roti	Bread	Bread (maida di)
Brown bread (whole wheat flour bread)	Atta bread	Brown bread	Brown bread		Chot	Godum podam bread			Godhumai bread	Godhuma pindi bread
Banana (ripe)	Kala (paka)	Kela	Kela	Bale hannu	Kel	Vazha pazham	Kelee	Champaa kadali	Vazha pazham	Arati pandu
Besan / Bengal gram flour	Bashun (kolai shuti)	Channa atta	Besan	Kadalai hittu	Besan	Kadalai maav	Besan	Besan	Kadalai maav	Senaga pindi
Banglore brinjal	— See chow chow marrow / cho-cho marrow									
Cashew nuts	Hijli (kaju) badam	Kaju	Kaju	Geru beeja (Godambe)	Kaju	Kasaundi	Kaju	Lanka ambu manji	Mundiri paruppu	Jeedi pappu

NAMES AND LANGUAGES CHART

Common Name	Bengali	Gujarati	Hindi	Kannada	Kashmiri	Malayalam	Marathi	Oriya	Tamil	Telugu
Cream of milk	Dudhir shor	Doodh ki malai	Malai	Kere Kene	Malayi	Pada	Malai	Sara	Paal aadai	Pala Meegada
Curd (yoghurt)	Duyi (dodhi)	Dahi	Dahi	Mosaru	Zaamut duad	Thayir	Dahi	Dahi	Thayir	Perugu
Cucumber	Sasha (Shosha)	Kakdi	Kakdi / kheera	Southai kayi	Laa'r	Vellari kai	Kaakdi	Kakudi	Kakkari kai	Dosa kayi (kakdi)
Cardamom	Elaichi (choto/ bado)	Elaichi	Elaichi (choti/badi)	Yelakki	Aa'l budu'a aal	Elathari	Veldode	Alaichi	Elakkai	Elakkayi
Cinnamon	Daruchini (Dalchini)	Dalchini	Dalchini	Dalchini	Dalchin	Patta	Dalchini	Dalchini	Luvanga pattai	Dasini chakka
Clove	Labango	Lavang	Lavang	Lavanga	Ruang	Grambu	Lavang	Labang	Kirambu	Lavangalu
Coriander Seed	Dhania (dhone)	Dhania (kothmir libdhana)	Dhania (sabut)	Kothambari beejai	Daaniwal	Kothambari	Dhane	Dhania	Kothamalli varai	Dhaniyalu
Coriander leaves	Dhone pata	Kothmer dhana	Hara dhaniya	Kotambari soppu	Daaniwal	Kothamalli yela	Kothimbir	Dhania patra	Kothamalli yelai	Kothimiri
Cumin seed	Zira	Jiru	Jeera (safed)	Jeerige	Zyur	Jeerakam (jeeram)	Jire	Jira	Jeeragam	Jeelakarra

NAMES AND LANGUAGES CHART

Common Name	Bengali	Gujarati	Hindi	Kannada	Kashmiri	Malayalam	Marathi	Oriya	Tamil	Telugu
Curry leaves	Barsanga (curry patta)	Mitha limbdo	Kadipatta (meetha neem)	Kari berine soppu	—	Karivepille	Kadilimbe	Barsanga patna	Karve pilai	Karve paku
Cherry	Cherry phal				khlass	Cherry	Cherries	Cherry	—	Cherry
Celery — A type of salad leaf										
Currant / sultana / munakka / Black currant — Larger variety than kismis, of dried grapes with seeds										
Corn flour (refined / whole)	Corn flour Sukhno battar beshun	Makaino lot		Musikina jolada hittu	Makai oat	Chola podi	Makaiche peeth	Makka atta	Solapodi	Mokkazonna pindi
Cabbage	Bandhako-pee	Kobi	Bandh gobi (patta gobi)	Yela kosu (mutte kosu)	Band gobhi	Muttacose	Kobi	Bandha kobi	Muttaikosu (Kose keerai)	Goskura (cabbage)
Capsicum (giant chilli)	Lanka (bilathi) / Shimla morich	Mota mircha	Simla (pahadi) mirch	Dodda (donna) mensinkai	Marcha wangun	Unda mulagu	Bhopla (Mothya) mirchi	Simla Marich	Koda milaga	Bondu pachi mirapakai

293

NAMES AND LANGUAGES CHART

Common Name	Bengali	Gujarati	Hindi	Kannada	Kashmiri	Malayalam	Marathi	Oriya	Tamil	Telugu
Carrot	Gajor	Gajara	Gajar	Gajari (Pechana)	Gazzur	Carrot	Gajar	Manjal mullangi		Carrot / gajara gadda
Cauliflower	Phool kopee (gobi)	Phul kobi	Gobi or phool gobi	Hoovakosu (hukosu)	Phool gobi	Kobi flower	Phul kobi	Phul kobi	Kovippu	Kosugadda (cauliflower)
Chow-chow (Cho-Cho marrow) (Bangalore brinjal)			Vilayati baingan / lanku	Seeme badnekai				Phuti kakudi	Seemai kathirikai	Seema / Banglore vankayi
Cluster beans	Jhar sim (choto sim)	Govar	Gwar ki phali	Gorikayi		Kothavara	Gwar chi phali / govari	Guanra chhuin	Kothave-rangai	Gor chikkudu kai
Colocasia/ Colocasia leaves	Kochumu-khi (pata)	Alvi (pata)	Arvi (patre)	Keshave (Samagadde)	Arbi	Chembu (yella)	Alu kanda (Alucha ganthi) (paan)	Saru (patra)	Chembu Chelong kilangi (elai)	Chaama dumpa (akulu)
Corn(fresh) / corn cob (maize cob) (tender)	Kacha butta	Makai	Bhutta	Vorogida / musikkinu (jola) Vanagidha	Makaa'y	Unakku (patha malla) cholam	Makkya che kanase	Makaa	Makka cholam	Mokka jonna pottu

NAMES AND LANGUAGES CHART

Common Name	Bengali	Gujarati	Hindi	Kannada	Kashmiri	Malayalam	Marathi	Oriya	Tamil	Telugu
China grass	— See Agar Agar									
Chikkoo	Shabeda	Chiku	Chiku	Chikkoo / Sapota	Chikoo	Sapota	Chiku	Sapta	Sapota	Sapota
Cereal	Aanaj	Kathod	Anaaj			Dhanyam	Dhanya	Anaaj	Dhanyam	Dhanyam
Cheese	Chaana	Cheese	Paneer	Vadeda halu	Chaaman	Cheese	Cheese	Chena		Palavirugudu
Custard apple	Ata phal	Ata	Sharifa	Seethaphalam		Seetha phazham (aat nakka)	Sita phal	Ata / sita phala	Seetha Phazham	Seetha phala pandu
Drumstick	Saijna danta (shojne)	Saragavo	Saijan / shehjowe ki phali	Nuggekai		Muringakkai	Shevya chi sheng	Saijina chui	Murunga kai	Mulakkada
Dalia (coarse wheat rava) / broken wheat	Dalia	Gauna na phadiya	Dalia	Jave godi ravae	Dalia	—	—	Dala	ravai	Mutuka godhuma ravai
Dough	Makha atta	Bandhe lo lot / pinda	Goonda hua atta	Kalasida hirtu (Kanaka)	Oat	Gothambu maav	Mallele peeth	Dola atta	Pisaindha maav	Kalipina pindi

NAMES AND LANGUAGES CHART

Common Name	Bengali	Gujarati	Hindi	Kannada	Kashmiri	Malayalam	Marathi	Oriya	Tamil	Telugu
Frying-pan	Tava	Tavodi (lodhi)	Tava	Henchu	Tav	Cheena chatti	Tava	Tava	Erumbu-satti	Penamu
Dry ginger (sonth)	Shukno ada	Soonth	Sonth	Sunti	Sonth	Chuth	Soonth	Shunthi	Sukku	Sonthi
Dates (fresh)	Khajur	Khajur	Khajur	Bend kajura	Khajur	Entranda pazham	Khajur	Khajini	Pericham pazham	Kajjura pandu
Dhruva grass	Durba ghash		Doob ghas		Dharv thooj		Durva ghaas	Durbo ghaso	Aruham pul	Durva
Dry coconut	— See Copra									
Essence	Essence	Essence	Khushboo	Suvaasane	Suvasana	Suvas	Essence	—	—	Suvasana
Elephant yam		— See Yam (elephant)								
Fenugreek seeds	Methi	Methi	Methi	Menthiya beeje	Meeth	Uluva	Methi	Methi	Menthiyam (ventha-yam)	Menthulu
Fenugreek leave	Methi saag	Methi	Methi saag	Menthiya soppu	Methi	Uluva ila	Methi	Methi saag	Methiya keerai	Menthi koora
Fig	Dumoor	Anjeer	Anjeer	Anjura	Anjeer	Atti pazham	Anjeer	Dimiri	Atti pazham	Attipandu

NAMES AND LANGUAGES CHART

Common Name	Bengali	Gujarati	Hindi	Kannada	Kashmiri	Malayalam	Marathi	Oriya	Tamil	Telugu
Flat / Broad / Sword beans	— See broad beans									
Fruit	Phal	Phal	Phal	Phala hannu	Phal	Pazham	Phal	Phal	Pazham / pazhangal	Pallu
French beans	—	Fansi	Bakla phal /fras bean	Huruli kayi	Fraa'sh bean	—	Pharas bee	—	—	Beans
Fresh corn (fresh)	— See Corn (fresh)									
Fresh Coriander leaves	— See Coriander leaves									
Fresh Coconut	Narkole	Nariyal	Nariyal	Tenginkai	Narjeel	Tenga	Kacha naral	Nadiya	Thengai	Kobbari
Green gram (whole)	Mung	Mag	Moong (sabut)	Hesaru kalu	Muang	Cherupa-yaru	Mug	Muga	Pachai (paasi) payaru	Pesalu
Green gram (split)	Mung dal	Mug dal	Moong dal	Hesaru bele	Muang dal	Cherupa-yaru parippu	Mug dal	Mung daal	Payatham (paasi) parippu	Pesara pappu
Ghee	Ghee	Ghee	Ghee	Thuppa	Dhyaav	Ney	Thup	Gheea	Neyyi	Neyyi

NAMES AND LANGUAGES CHART

Common Name	Bengali	Gujarati	Hindi	Kannada	Kashmiri	Malayalam	Marathi	Oriya	Tamil	Telugu
Guava	Payra	Jam phal	Amrud	Sebae hannu (chepae)	Amrud	Perakka	Peru	Pijuli	Koya pazham	Jama pandu
Gravy	Jhol	—	Rasa	—	Ras	Chara	Rasa	Jhola	Kanzi / kootu	Palchatidi
Green peas	Bilati shunti / matar	Watana	Matar	Seemai batani	Matar' (kara)	English payru	Hirwe vatana	Matara	Pachai pataani	Pachi batani
Goosefoot white	Bathe saag	Chilni bhaji	Bathua saag	Sakothina soppu	—	Koluppa cherai	Chandan bathua	Bathua saag	—	—
Grape	Angoor	Drakha	Angur	Drakhsa	Da'ch	Mundiriga	Drakshe	Angur	Draksha	Draksha
Gram flour	— See Besan									
Gooseberry	— See Indian gooseberry or amla									
Garnish	Shajano	—	Sajaawat	—	Sajaawat	Alankaram	Sajawane	Shajao	Alankaram	Alankaram
Garlic	Rashun	Lasun	Lehsun	Bellulli	Ruhan	Vellulli	Lasoon	Rasuna	Ullipoondu	Vellullipai
Ginger (fresh)	Adu (ada)	Ada / adu	Adrak	Ona (hasi) shunti	Adrak	Inji	Ale	Ada	Inji	Allamu
Groundnut/ peanut/ monkeynut	China badam	Bhoising	Mung phali	Kadalaikai	Muang phali	Neela kadelai	Sengdane	China badam	Nila kadalai	Verusenaga kai

NAMES AND LANGUAGES CHART

Common Name	Bengali	Gujarati	Hindi	Kannada	Kashmiri	Malayalam	Marathi	Oriya	Tamil	Telugu
Green chilli	Kancha laanka	Marcha	Hari mirch	Mensin kai	March vangan	Pacha mulaga	Hirvi mirch	Kancha lanka	Pache molahai	Pachi mirapakai
Honey	Mau		Shaid (madhu)	Tentuppa (Jamatuppa)	Maanch	Then	Madh	—	Then	Thene
Hydrogena-ted oil	Banaspati	Vanaspati	Vanaspati (dalda)	—	Dhayav	—	Vanaspati	—	Dalda	Dalda
Indian gooseberry / amla (big/small)	Amlaki	Amla	Amla	Nellikayi (Belta/Kiru)	Amla	Nellika (chiru)	Awla	Amla	Nellikai (chiru)	Usirikai
Jaggery	Gud	Gol	Gud	Bella	Gor	Vellum	Gul	Guda	Vellam	Bellam
Jackfruit	Echore (Pak kanthal)	Phunus	Kathal	Halasu	Kathal	Chakka	Phanas	Panasa	Pala pazham	Panasa kayi
Jowar	Juar	Juar	Juar	Jola	Jowar	Cholam	Jwari	Janha	Cholam	Jonnalu
Jambul	Kalojam	Jambu	Jamun	Neralai		Naga pazham	Jambhool	Jamu koli	Naga pazham	Neredi pandu
Knol Khol	Ol kopi	Nol kol	Ganth gobi (khol rabi)	Navili kosu	Mo'nd	Nool kol	Naval kol (knol khol)	Ul kobi		Naval kolu

NAMES AND LANGUAGES CHART

Common Name	Bengali	Gujarati	Hindi	Kannada	Kashmiri	Malayalam	Marathi	Oriya	Tamil	Telugu
Kundru (gherkin)	Telakuchu	Tindori (ghole gluru)	Kandori (kindori / kunthru)	Tondekai	–	Kovakka	Thondli	Kunduru	Kovakkai	Donda kai
Copra / dry coconut	Shukno narkel	Suku nariyal	Snkha nariyal (kopra)	Ona koppari	Narjeel	Kopra	Kopra	Sukhula nadia	Koprai	Yendu kobbari
Khatta palak saag	–	–	khatta palak saag	chukkai soppu	O'bj	–	Ambat chukka	–	Chukka Keerai	chukka koora
Lady's fingers	Dherosh	Bhinda	Bhindi	Bende kai	Bindu	Vendakka	Bhendi	Bhendi	Vendai kai	Benda kayi
Lentil (whole / split)	Masoor Musur	Masur (dal)	Masur (dal)	Masura payaru / bele (chandra bele)	Musur	Masur parippu	Masur / dal	Masura	Mysore parippu	Misur pappu (yerra kandi pappu)
Lime (sweet)	Musami	Musammi	Musambi	Kittile	Musambi		Mosambi	Musammi	Elimichi pallam/kai	Battayi pandu
Lime / Lemon	Lebu	Kadigi limbu (lehrer)	Neembu	Nimbe	Nyomb	Cherua ranga	Nimbu	Gonga kulia lembu	Elumuchai kai	Nimma kai

NAMES AND LANGUAGES CHART

Common Name	Bengali	Gujarati	Hindi	Kannada	Kashmiri	Malayalam	Marathi	Oriya	Tamil	Telugu
Lettuce	Salad patta	Salat	Salad patta		Salaad	Uvar cheera	Salad chi paan	Salathu		Kavu
Lemon grass	—	—	—	—	—	—	Goutichah (ghas)	—	—	Nimma gaddi
Mushroom	Paatal kot	—	Gucchi	Naaye chatri	Hedar	—		Chati	Kalaan	Kukka godugu
Millet	Kangri	Ral kang	Kangri	—	Shol	Thina	Rala	—	Thenai	Korralu
Mango (raw / ripe)	Aam (kancha / pucca)	Keri	Aam (kacha / pucca)	Mavina (kai / hannu)	Amb	Mam (kai / phazham)	Amba (kacha / pucca)	Amba	Mam (kai / pazham)	Mamidi (kai / pandu)
Mint	Pudina saag.	Fudina	Paudina	Pudina	Pudynu	Mint	Pudeena	Podana patra	Pothina	Pudina
Mace (Javitri)	Javitri	Jaavantri (Jay patri)	Javitri	Jai patre	Jalwatur	Jathi pathri	Jay patri	Javitri	Jathi patri	Japatri
Mustard seed	Sorse	Rai	Rai	Sasive (sasuve)	Assur	Kadugu	Rayee (mohri)	Sorisa	Kadugu	Aavaalu
Mustard leaves	Sorse shak	—	Sarson ka saag	Sasive elai (sopu)	—	—	Rayi che patte	Soriso saag	Kadugu keerai	Aava aku
Mango powder	— See Amchur									

NAMES AND LANGUAGES CHART

Common Name	Bengali	Gujarati	Hindi	Kannada	Kashmiri	Malayalam	Marathi	Oriya	Tamil	Telugu
Musk melon	Khormuj	—	Kharbooja	—	—	—	Kharbuj	—	Vellari pazham	Kharbuja pandu
Maida (refined wheat flour)	Maida	Maida	Maida	Hittu maida	Maide	Maida maavu	Maida	Moide	Maida maavu	Maida pindi
Nutmeg	Jaiphal	Jayphal	Jaiphal	Jajikai (jogakai)	Zaaphal	Jartukai	Jaiphal	Jaiphalo	Jathi kai	Jaji kai
Neem	Neem	Limda	Neem	Bevu	Neem	Aryaveppila	Kadu limb	Nima	Veppilai	Vepa
Orange	Kamala lebu	Santra	Santra (narangi)	Kithilai	Sangtar	Madhura naranga	Santre	Kamala	Aranji (Kichili) pazham	Kamala pandu
Onion	Pyaz	Dungli (Kando)	Pyaaz	Erulli / neerulli	Gand	Ulli	Kanda	Piaza	Vengayam	Nirulli (ullipayi)
Onion shoots	Payaj / kauli	Dunglina dakhadi	Hara pyaz	Erulli soppu	Gand ke patte	Ulliera thandu	Kandya chi paat	Piaza sandha	Vengayam yelai (thandu)	Ulli kollu
Onion seed	Kalojire	Kala jeera	Kalaunji	Erulli beeja	Kalaunji		Kandya chya biya	Kalo jeera	Vengayam vidhai	Ullipai ginzalu
Parsley	— A type of salad leaf									

302

NAMES AND LANGUAGES CHART

Common Name	Bengali	Gujarati	Hindi	Kannada	Kashmiri	Malayalam	Marathi	Oriya	Tamil	Telugu
Parwal	Patol	Padwal	Parwal			Potalam	Parwar	Potala		Kommu potla or linga potla kai
Pear	Nashpati	Nashpati	Nashpati	Berikai	Tang	Sabarjil	Nashpati	Nashpati	Berikai	Berikai
Pulses	Dal	Daal	Daale		Dal	Parippukal	Dalee	Dal	Parappu	Pappulu
Peppercorns	Mari (gol marich)	Mari (gol marich)	Kali mirchi (gol mirch)	Kari menasu	Marya machrs / maruters (march)	Kuru mulaki ?	Mire	Gol (kala) marich (kali miri)	Milagu	Miriyalu
Poppy seed (khus khus)	Postho	Khus khus (aphani)	Khus khus (post dara)	gas gase (afim)	khus khus	Khasa khas (afima)	Khas khas	Poshthak	Khasa khasa	Gasagasalu
Potato	Alu	Batata	Alu	(Urula) Alu gadde	Oloe	Urula kizhangu	Batata	Alu	Uralai kilanga	Urlagadda (alugadda / bangala dumpa)
Pomegranate (seed)	Dalimer (daana)		Anaar (ka daana)	Dalimbave (beeja)	Anar (dan)	Mathala Naranga	Dalimba (che dane)	Dalimba (manjee)	Mathulam (vidhai)	Danimma (ginzalu)

NAMES AND LANGUAGES CHART

Common Name	Bengali	Gujarati	Hindi	Kannada	Kashmiri	Malayalam	Marathi	Oriya	Tamil	Telugu
Papaya (ripe)	Pepe (paka)	Papaya	Papita	Phanangi	Kel	Omakai	Popai	Amrut bhanda (pachila)	Poppak	Boppai pandu
Pineapple	Anarash	Ananas	Ananas	Ananas		Kayitti chekka	Ananas	Sapuri anasianas	Anasi pazham	Anasa pandu
Peach		Aadu	Aarhoo	Mara sebu	Tsun'u		Peach	Piccuu		
Plum	Alubokhara	Alubokhara	Alubokhara		Laar	Alubokhar			Alapagoda / alubhakar	Alapagoda
Puffed rice	Muri (mudi)	Mumra / murmura	Murmura	Puri	Murmura	Pori	Murmure	Mudhi	Arisi pori	Murmaralu
Roasted Bengal gram	Chol bhaja	Phutana	Bhuna chana	Huri kadale	Chan	Varutha kadale	Phutana chana	Bhaja buta	Portu kadalai	Putnala pappu (gulla senaga pappu)
Raw papaya	Kancha pempe	Papayi	Kacha papita	Parangi		Omakaya	Kacha papaya	Kancha amrut bhanda	pappali kai	Boppai kai/bobbasi kai

NAMES AND LANGUAGES CHART

Common Name	Bengali	Gujarati	Hindi	Kannada	Kashmiri	Malayalam	Marathi	Oriya	Tamil	Telugu
Raw banana / plantain (raw)	Kanche kala	Kele	Kela (hara)	Balekkai	Kel	Vazhakkai	KachiKeli	Bantala (kancha) kadali	Vazhak kai	Arati kai
Pumpkin red	Kumra	Kohlu	Kaddu (sitaphal)	Sihi kumblakai (kumhala)	Paa'rimalor all	Mathan	Lal bhopla	Kakharu	Parangi kai	Gummidi kai
Radish	Mulo / mula	Mula	Muli	Mullangi	Muj	Mullangi chakkara	Mula	Mula	Mullengi	Mullangi
Raisin (kishmish)	Kishmish	Kismish	Kismish	Drakshi	Kishmish	Mundiringa (unakku)	Manukka	Kishmish	Drakshai	Kismis (yendu draksha)
Red Chilli	Shukno lonka	Lal marcha	Lal mirchi	Kempu mensin kai	Mars vangan	Vattal mulaku	Lal mirchi	Lal marich	Milagai vattal	Yerra (yendu) mirapakai
Refined wheat flour	— See Maida									
Raspberry		Raspberry	Rushberry		Rushbhery					
Raw Jack fruit	Aanchar	Kawla phanas	Kathal	Halasinkai	Kathal	Idichakka	Kacha phanas (kawla)	Panasa katha	Chakkai (pilapinju)	Panasa kayi

NAMES AND LANGUAGES CHART

Common Name	Bengali	Gujarati	Hindi	Kannada	Kashmiri	Malayalam	Marathi	Oriya	Tamil	Telugu
Ridge gourd	Jhinge / jhinga	Turia	Torai	Hirekai (heera kai)	Turrich	Peechinge (pottika)	Dod ka	Janchi	pirrkan kai	Beera kai
Red gram (pigeon pea)	Arhar dal	Tur tuverni dal	Arhar dal / tur dal	Thugare bele	Arhar dal	Thuram parippu	Toorchi dal	Harada	Tuvaram parippu	Kandi pappu
Ragi	Madua	Ragi bhav	Madua (okta)	Ragi	Ragi	Moothari (kotta)	Nachni	Mandia	Kezhvaragu	Ragulu
Raw rice (milled)	Atap chowl (khol chatta)	choka	Arua chaval	Mingae hakidu (polish akki)	Pra'n	Velutha ari	Tandul sadlela	Arua chawula	Vellaiputtu arisi	Millu (tella) biyyam
Raw rice (hand-pounded)	Atap chowl (dheki chatta)	Choka (hathra chandela)	Arwa chaval	Kotnuda akki	Tomul	Ari	Tandool haathani kutlela	Chaula	Kai kuthu pachai arisi	Dampudu biyyam
Red cabbage	— A dark-reddish-violet variety of cabbage									
Rice (puffed) / puffed rice	Muri (mudi)	Mumra / murmura	Murmura	Puri	Murmura	Pori	Murmura	Mudhi	Arisi pori	Murmaralu
Rice flour	Chaler gudo	Chokha nu	Chawal ka atta	Akki hirtu	Tumul	Ari podi	Tandula chi peeth	Chaula gunda	Arisi maav	Biyyapu pindi

NAMES AND LANGUAGES CHART

Common Name	Bengali	Gujarati	Hindi	Kannada	Kashmiri	Malayalam	Marathi	Oriya	Tamil	Telugu
Rajmah	Rajmah	Phanasi	Rajmah	Tingela heri	Razmaha					Barigalu
Sago	Saboo	Sabudana	Sabudana	Sabakki	Saboodana	Sago	Sabudana	Sagudana	Javv arisi	Saggu biyyam
Sweet lime (musambi)	Mushumbi / musami	Musambi/ musammi	Musambi	Kirtile	Musambi	Musambi	Musamba	Musammi	Musambi	Musambi (bathayi kai)
Sultana / munakka / currant	Kismis	Kismish	Munakka	Vana dodda Bejaeruva Drakshi	Kismis		Munakka	Kismis		Yendu pedda draksha (ginzalu kalavi)
Salt	Labon	Nimak	Nimak	Uppu	Noon	Upp.	Meeth	Luna	Uppu	Uppu
Saffron	Jaffran	Kesar	Kesar	Kesari (kum kuma huvva)	Kong	Kunguna poo	Kesar	Saffron	Kum kuma poo	Kumkuma puvu
Sesame seed gingelly seeds	Til	Tal	Til	Yellu (acchellu)	Til	Yellu	Til	Rasi	Ellu	Nuvvulu
Sesame oil	Tiler tel	Tal nu tel	Til ka tel	Yellene	Teel	Nallenna	Tila cha tel	Rasi tel	Nallyennai	Nuvvula nooni

NAMES AND LANGUAGES CHART

Common Name	Bengali	Gujarati	Hindi	Kannada	Kashmiri	Malayalam	Marathi	Oriya	Tamil	Telugu
Semolina (suji)	Suji	Ravo	Sooji	Rava	Soozi	Rava	Rava	Suji	Ravai	Bombayi rawa
Spices	Moshla	Garam masala	Garam masala	Masala samanu	Masal		Garam masala	Mashla	Vasannai diraviyam	Masala samanulu
Smooth / sponge gourd	Dhundal	Turia	Turai	Tuppatura kai (Hiraykai)	Turai	Katupee-chal	Shiral (ghosala)	Janhi	Peera kangai (mozhugu)	Nethi beerakai / guthi beerakai
Snake gourd	Chichinga	Pandola	Chachinda (cheechinda)	Podavala kaya		Podavalanga	Padwal	Chachinda	Pudavalan gai	Potla kayi
Spinach	Palang sag	Palak	Palak	Dantina soppu / basala	Paalakh	Basala chora	Mayalu / palak	Palang sag	Pasalai keerai / kothu pasalai	Palakura / dumpa bachali
String / slender beans		Chola	Lobia	Halsande kai		Acchinga pavar	Chavali	Jhudunga	Thatta kai	Barbati
Sweet potato	Rangaalu	Sakkaria	Shakar kand	Genasu	Shakar Kand	Chakkara kizhangu valli	Ratale	Kandamula / sakar kand	Chakkarai velli kilangu	Sila gada dumpa

NAMES AND LANGUAGES CHART

Common Name	Bengali	Gujarati	Hindi	Kannada	Kashmiri	Malayalam	Marathi	Oriya	Tamil	Telugu
Soya bean	Gari kalai	Soya	Bhatmas		Muth	Soya bean	Soya			
Sugar candy	Michri	Sakar	Misri	Kallu sakkera	Nabad	Kalkandam		Misri	Kalkandu	Patika bellam
Sugar cane juice	Ikhu raush	Sherdina ras	Ganne ka ras	Kobbina halu	Gan ras	Karumbin neeru	Usacha ras	Akhju ras dorua	Karuppan charu	Cheruku rasam
Salad	Salad	Kachumber	Kachumber	Kosambri soppu	Salam		Koshimbir	Salad		Pachi kooralu/pallu
Soup	Sap	Soup	Shorba	Soup	Soup	Soup	Rasa	Soup		
Shajira	— See Black cumin seeds									
Sapota	— See Chikkoo									
Syrup	Chinir rash	Chasni	Chasni	Paaka	Chasni / madred poon	Paani	Paak	Chini sika	Pagu	Paakamu
Safflower seed	Kusum	Kusumbo	Kardi	Kusambe			Karadai		Sendurakan	Kusuma ginzalu
Sunflower seed	Suraj mukhi	Suraj mukhi	Surya mukhi	Surya kanti beeja		Surya kanti	Surya mukhi	Surya mukha pa manjee	Surya kanti	Poddu thirugudu ginzalu

NAMES AND LANGUAGES CHART

Common Name	Bengali	Gujarati	Hindi	Kannada	Kashmiri	Malayalam	Marathi	Oriya	Tamil	Telugu
Skimmed milk / defatted milk	Makhan tana doodh		Malai nikala hua doodh	Kane thegadha-halu	Gurus	Pada kalan ya pal		Sara kadha dudha	Kudaintha pal	Venna thesina palu
Tamarind	Tetul	Tentul (amli)	Imli	Hunise hannu	Tambe'r	Puli	Chinch	Tentuli	Puli	Chinta pandu
Tamarind extract / pulp	Tetul gola jol (ghono)	Amli nupaani	Imli ka ras	Hunise rasa (gojju)	Tamber		Chinche cha ras	Tentuli raas	Puli thanni	Chinta pandu gujju
Thyme (ajwain)	Joan	Ajmo (joan)	Ajwain	Oma	Jaawani (ajwain)	Omam (ayamotha-kam)	Onva (ova)	juyani	Omam	Vamu
Turmeric	Haldhar (Holud)	Haldhar	Haldi	Arshina (anashina)	Lader	Manjal	Huldi (halad)	Haladi	Manjal	Pasupu
Tinda / round gourd / dil pasand	Tinda	Tadabudr	Dil pasand				Dhepsun			
Tender coconut water	Daab	Leela nariyal nu paani	Nariyal ka paani	Elaneeru	Narjeel poon	Karikin valam	Narala cha paani	Pando paani	Elanner	Bomdamu neeru

NAMES AND LANGUAGES CHART

Common Name	Bengali	Gujarati	Hindi	Kannada	Kashmiri	Malayalam	Marathi	Oriya	Tamil	Telugu
Tomato	Tomato	Vilayathi vengam	Tamatar	Gudae hannu	Ruwangum	Takkali pazham	Tamate (velvangi)	Tamato	Takali palam	Tomato
Turnip	Shalgam ol kopi		Shalgam		Guagu		Shalgam	Shalgam		
Til	— See Sesame seeds									
Tej patta	— See Bay leaf									
Vermicelli (Semya)	Sevai (semai)		Sevayya (siwain)	Shevige	Ku'nu'	Semiya	Shevaya	Simai	Semiya	Semiya
Vinegar			Sirka	Kadale huli	Sirka	Vinagiri	Sirka			
Vegetables	Shobji		Sabjiyaa	Tarkari kai/palya	Sabzi	Paccha kari	Bhajia	Paniba	Kai kari	Kooralu
Wood apple	Kathbel	Kothu	Kaitha	Beleda kai/hannu		Vilam pazham	Kavath	Kaitha	Vilam pazham	Velaga pandu
Wheat	Gomasta (gom)	Gahu (ghau)	Gehun	Godhi	Ku'nu'kh	Gendum (muzhu gothambu)	Gahu	Gahama	Godhumai	Godhumalu
Whole wheat flour	Atta (Jata bhanga)	Ato	Ata (bina chhana hua)	Godhi hittu	Oth	Gothombu maavu	Gahucha peeth / kaneek	Atta	Muzhu godhmai maavu	Godhuma pindi

NAMES AND LANGUAGES CHART

Common Name	Bengali	Gujarati	Hindi	Kannada	Kashmiri	Malayalam	Marathi	Oriya	Tamil	Telugu
Whole wheat flour bread	— See Brown bread									
Walnut	Akhrot	Akhrot	Akhrot		Doon	Akhrod	Akhrot	Ahkoot	Akhrot	
Water melon	Tormuj	Tarbooj	Tarbooj	Kallangare hannu	Hend vend	Thanni mathanga	Kalingad	Tanabhuj	Tharpoo-shani pazham	Puchakkai
Wax gourd	— See Ash gourd / ash pumpkin									
Wheat grass	6-8" long shoots of wheat									
Yam (elephant)	Ol	Suran	Zaminkand	Dodda Suvarna gadda		Chenai (Valuthu)	Suran	Hathi khojia alu	Chenai (senai) khazangu	Kanda (dumpa)
Yeast		Khamir	Khameer			Yeast	Khamir		Khadi	
Yoghurt	— See Curds									
Whey	Chanar jhol		Chach	Vadadha kalina neeru				Chena pani		Pala virugudu neellu (theta neeru)

Bibliography

1. *Aahar Hee Aushadh Hai* by Dr. Heeralal.
   Swasthya Prakashan, Unnao (UP), 1990.
2. *Aahar Aur Swasthya* by Dr. Heeralal.
   Swastya Prakashan, Unnao (UP), 1990.
3. *Dakshin Bharat Dishes* by Jaya V. Shenoy.
   Saraswatha Prakashana, Udupi-2, D.K. India, 1992.
4. *Eating For Health* by L. Ganesa Sarma.
   Sarmaanugraha, Ganesh Nagar, Pudukkotai, 1978.
5. *Food For Health* by A.P. Dewan.
   A.C. Specialist Publishers (Pvt.) Ltd., New Delhi, 1991.
6. *Food That Heals* by H.K. Bakhru.
   Orient Paper Backs, New Delhi, 1990.
7. *Nutrition, India's Vital Problem* by Aslam Effendi.
   Prakrutti Chikitsa Pustakalaya, Bezwada, 1948.
8. *Nutritive Value of Indian Foods* by G. Gopalan, B.V. Rama Sastri
   and B.C. Balasubramanian, National Institute of Nutrition, ICMR,
   Hyderabad, 1996.
9. *Sprouts For Beauty, Youth and Health* by J.D. Vaish. New Delhi
10. *Swasthya Ke Liye Phal Turkariya* by Vitthal Das Modi.
    Prakashak Arogya Mandir, Gorakhpur.
    Mudrak, Ashok Kudran Grah, 42 Tashkand Marg, Allahabad, 1988.
11. *Your Family Friend*, January to May, 1996.
    Published, Printed, owned by Shri G.K. Seetharaman, 142,
    Zamrudpur (Opp. LSR College), New Delhi-110048, 1996.
12. *Diet And Good Health* by Dugald Semple.
    London: The C.W. Daniel Company, First edition, April, 1925.
13. *A Text Book of Household Arts* by Stella Soundararaj.
    Published by V. Abdulla; Orient Longman, Madras. Reprinted 1979.
14. *Better Homes* by M.A. Needham and A. G. Strong.
    Revised by Dr (Mrs) Rajammal P. Deva Das, Coimbatore. 4th
    edition. Calcutta. Oxford University Press, 1970

Index